THE DEATH OF DAVID DEBRIZZI

Also by Paul Micou

THE MUSIC PROGRAMME
THE COVER ARTIST

PAUL MICOU

THE ~~LIFE~~  *Death*
OF
DAVID
DEBRIZZI

BANTAM PRESS

LONDON · NEW YORK · TORONTO · SYDNEY · AUCKLAND

TRANSWORLD PUBLISHERS LTD
61-63 Uxbridge Road, London W5 5SA

TRANSWORLD PUBLISHERS (AUSTRALIA) PTY LTD
15-23 Helles Avenue, Moorebank, NSW 2170

TRANSWORLD PUBLISHERS (NZ) LTD
Cnr Moselle and Waipareira Aves,
Henderson, Auckland

Published 1991 by Bantam Press
a division of Transworld Publishers Ltd
Copyright ©Paul Micou 1991

The right of Paul Micou to be identified
as the author of this work has been asserted in accordance
with sections 77 and 78 of the Copyright Designs and Patents
Act 1988

British Library Cataloguing in Publication Data
Micou, Paul
The death of David Debrizzi
1. Title
813.54 [F]

ISBN 0-593-02362-5

Typeset in Garamond by Chippendale Type Ltd, Otley, West Yorkshire.
Printed in Great Britain by Mackays of Chatham Plc, Chatham, Kent

For Anna U

Dear Sir Geoffrey,

Before I reach the body of what I hope will be a brief letter, let me extend my congratulations on your knighthood. My warmest regards to Mary - that is, to Lady Flynch - who must be so relieved.

Geoffrey, I am incensed. You will have guessed that I now hold in my hands a copy of your *Life of David Debrizzi*. I wish to take you to task, a project I would find onerous enough in my second language, without the nagging chest complaint that has taken me on an enforced holiday in Switzerland. At least at this time of year the Swiss sun and air provide a pleasant environment, out on the terrace facing the Grand Glacier, for the composing of one's thoughts. Sun and air? How you used to laugh at puns, Geoffrey.

My doctor, noting how exercised I became while reading your book for the first time, prised the volume from my hands; another copy was smuggled past his suspicious minions' eyes by my brother, who may have wished to torture me with its effects. Having survived two readings, and recovered a small portion of my health during a three-week period of deep thought, I am prepared to list my objections.

Have no fear that a copy of this letter will reach the desks of those publications that issued such glowing reviews of your 'biography'; my narrow and benign intention is to make you feel what I feel, that an injustice has been committed to paper. My doctor – you may have heard of him, he is German and his name rhymes with 'Pain' – has approved of my writing to you. He believes it may serve as therapy; besides, he knows

7

he cannot stop me from writing any more than he can stop me from smoking.

I want at the outset to clear up the matter of what you would no doubt call 'sour grapes': you knew I had attempted my own modest *Life of David Debrizzi*, which in fact I had intended to entitle *The Death of David Debrizzi*, when I lost my nerve and set the manuscript aside. This would have been at about the time word reached me that your own *Life*, pre-empting my *Death*, would shortly appear. Never have I begrudged you your *Life*, any more than you would deny me my *Death*. It is only unfortunate that the two works could not have appeared simultaneously – or sametimeously, as you used to put it – so that the literary and musical authorities could have drawn an informed comparison in my favour. Given the state of my health, and the treachery of my *bastard* of a British publisher – who loathes me merely because I am French – I feel it is safe to say that your *Life* will stand alone on the shelves for posterity, while my *Death* will remain untold.

Your

PART ONE

▮▮ ▮▮▮ ▮▮

THE DAWN
OF A GIFT

Your

CHAPTER ONE

I was intrigued by the form of your narrative, which is best summed up by quoting the first sentence: '*I met David Debrizzi on a wet November day in 1963, at his parents' house near St Germain.*' Starting a biography with the first-person-singular pronoun, you make the reader wonder at the outset if he will learn more about author than subject. This is probably post- or neo-something of you – you would know – and I suppose you deliberately sustained this tone to hold the interest of your London literary hangers-on, who care less about David Debrizzi than about the glamorous role you played in his life. If you were to count, as I have done, you would discover that the word 'I', that most fundamental typographical stroke, appears fifteen times in the first paragraph. While the reader learns nothing about David Debrizzi other than his parents' approximate address, he discovers the name of your favourite restaurant in the same neighbourhood, and is asked to ponder vague reminiscences of Parisian romance in times gone by. Marvellous. But if I quibble about every sentence or paragraph, this will be a long letter indeed.

*

You seem to have forgotten, Geoffrey, that on the morning you met David Debrizzi for the first time (I can endorse the date, the poor weather, the appearance of the Debrizzi household), I was the one who greeted you at the door.

I was ushered into a rather murky drawing room by a stooped old woman I later learned was David Debrizzi's grandmother.

Oh, really, Geoffrey? Was it a stooped old grandmother who took your hat and scarf and umbrella and overcoat and traded words of exasperation about the weather, in perfect English, who remarked to you that you looked taller than your concert posters, and who understood your quip about the light rain dripping on café awnings like pizzicato pluckings of cello strings? No, it was not a stooped old woman who ushered you inside; it was I. You seem to have no difficulty remembering that later you and 'a companion' stared at one another in disbelief at La Coupole, as word circulated that a certain world leader had been shot in America. Again, that was no mere companion who absorbed your grief; it was I. Given the disproportionate coverage of my role in David's (and your, and my) *Life*, I am surprised that you did not devote this section to describing your first meeting with *me*, which took up more time, and was rather more memorable given the circumstances, than the few minutes you spent paying your respects to the 'child prodigy'.

You compare your decision to leave London to that of the Magi in their part of the world: you had heard news of a marvel. A little boy lived there, you had been told, whose powers were miraculous. As to your description of first laying eyes on the seven-year-old David, let me say this: it is criminal.

I was guided down a dark corridor to the back of the dishevelled Debrizzi home, feeling an unaccountable foreboding, as if even then I believed myself predestined to become entwined in a remarkable life. The walls were covered with faded blue tissu *and reeked of centuries-old cabbage and potatoes. Ancient dark wood creaked underfoot. The house showed all the signs of the hard times upon which this stalwart family had fallen since the war – clutter and dust, and not a servant to be seen. I remember that I had to compose myself as David Debrizzi's asthmatic grandmother indicated that we had arrived at the door that would lead me into David's life. She pushed open the door and bade me enter. Into the gloomy little room I went. I was struck by its mustiness and lack of light; heavy tapestry curtains were drawn tightly across its one window; the grand piano was practically indistinguishable, looming blackly on the far side of the room - resonating with potential, as it were.*

A tiny interrogative 'Bonjour?' reached me from the darkest corner. There sat David Debrizzi, about whom I had heard such startling things, his small white face glowing like a moon in the darkness. Upon his knee was a hardbound edition of the Scherzi, *in which he had been engrossed . . .*

Unaccountable foreboding, indeed. My recollection of the event, which is as clear as the Swiss sky overhead, is that you were somewhat winded by your walk through the rain, and did not decline my invitation to join me for a *ballon de rouge*. We sat in the kitchen. You asked me my name and claimed to have heard of me – a transparent but no less charming lie. You asked me where David was, and I told you he was out buying bread with his grandmother, and would return shortly. You asked me if I thought this whole matter of hearing the child play the piano could be hurried along, that you had other business to attend to. You asked me if I would like to join you at La Coupole in the evening to answer questions about David, and to explain what course of instruction I had pursued so far. You told me that you had no intention of putting me out of a job, but that in certain cases a talent like David's – in which you showed no signs

13

of believing – had to be nursed along with the utmost care by the most experienced hands. I nodded dumbly to everything you said because I was, briefly, in awe of you. Remember that you were thirty and I was twenty-one. You seemed ancient to me, and your musical accomplishments were well known in Paris even then. I had done nothing of much use since quitting the piano except to engineer my disqualification from military service; I would do the same for David years later and have him exempted on the grounds of deafness – quite a nice touch, I thought, for a piano virtuoso.

When David finally returned with his 'stooped old woman' of a grandmother, it was to rush to me and give me a kiss. He had not seen me for nearly twenty minutes, after all. I instructed him to say hello and shake your hand, which he did. You looked at him sceptically, which almost everyone did in those days, and which he hated. You asked David if he had been told you were coming and he replied in the affirmative. He apologized for being late.

I did not dare at first to ask the child to play for me. I knew enough to approach him gingerly, to skirt about the edges of his formidable gift. I did not want to frighten him. I felt as if I had encountered a wet and wounded woodland creature that could not know I intended it no harm.

In fact – and I remember this as if it were five minutes ago, and have laughed about it with David since – you had no sooner said hello to the child than he ran into the light and airy drawing room – no musty dark; no grand piano either, just a little Gregory upright – and began to show off shamelessly for you. He played Chopin's Second Etude (Opus 10), which at first you thought was a disaster. You thought your trip to Paris had been a waste of time. Then you realized that he was playing the left hand a half-step down. This was one of David's little jokes.

When I saw your perplexed expression I tried to explain to you that David was not yet aware of Music, as you and

14

I understood it. He was aware of black and white keys and the noisy piece of furniture beneath his uncanny fingers. You pretended that his feat had not amazed you.

For nearly an hour I listened, rapt, to the most astounding gift I had ever encountered.

Yes, well, it has been more than twenty-five years now, and your memory must be washed out by the blazing light of your intervening successes. In fact, you listened to the single piece I mentioned, which David played so quickly that it could not have lasted more than a minute and a half, then asked me for your coat and hat and umbrella and scarf and made your farewells. You did not seem at all impressed.

That night at La Coupole, where I suppose you were justified in drinking as heavily as you did because the world had just lost a substantial leader, you went on at great length about the unreliability of early promise. These children often lost interest, you told me. You did not think you were the right man for the job, not yet, and wished me luck in seeing David through to 'the next level'. You did not say what this 'next level' entailed. You would come back in two years, you said. This mistake in your judgement goes unrecorded in your brief first chapter, and, miraculously, the next two years simply drop out of your narrative like smoke through a sieve, or whatever the expression is in English.

May I fill in those two years for you, and the 'dawn' of David's 'gift', before we move on together to your scandalous Chapter Two?

Your description of David's early years was apt enough, I suppose, for the purposes of a potted biography. Your section on David's first demonstration of unusual ability, while somewhat melodramatic, succeeded in conveying to the reader the magic of David's realization that the piano was his to master (as well it might, since you seem to have lifted this section verbatim from an article I wrote on the subject – in German – some twenty years ago). Still, several points rankle.

15

Imagine the surprise of David's parents when they seated four-year-old David on the piano bench, hoping to spark an early interest in music, only to see him launch into a rather complex and closely-harmonized fugue based on the 'Marseillaise'. Little did they know at the time, for mischievous David did not want to let on, that David had stood, rather than sat, at the piano for hours at a stretch when they were out of the house. Only the grandmother had witnessed this spectacle, and was clearly too deaf or senile to take notice.

You really seem to have it in for David's poor Corsican grandmother, whose name you never give. Her name is Greta Debrizzi, and you will be happy to hear that she is still alive. I was able to visit her on her ninety-sixth birthday, and even then she was neither senile nor deaf. The thoroughness of your researchers, who were capable of discovering and plagiarizing an obscure essay of mine (*Die Kunst ein Junges Genie zu Fordern*, 1969), does not seem to have extended in the same way to members of your subject's family. Greta Debrizzi could have told you that it was *she* who taught David to play his first simple tunes (the 'Marseillaise' fugue is a delightful idea; where did you get it?); it was she who played the little trick of not telling David's parents. In this way Greta was able to make David's musical initiation into a game.

His first performance was orchestrated like a conjurer's trick. His parents came home (from *work*, Geoffrey, from *work*; you make their daily absence seem like callous neglect). They opened a litre of wine. They seated themselves as usual near the fire, to enjoy each other's company and to prepare themselves for the agony of getting David off to bed before dinner. David appeared, scrubbed and bubbly, and said good evening in the formal way his grandmother had taught him. His cue came when his mother asked him what he had learned at school that day. He replied, as usual, that he had been cuffed across the cheek for sloppy penmanship, then added that he had learned to play the piano. His parents laughed. David grinned at his grandmother and took his place, standing, at the keyboard. He had been practising in secret for several weeks, and was able not only to play a long medley of the usual children's songs, including 'Frère Jacques' and 'Sur Le Pont d'Avignon', but a slightly reworked 'Träumerei' as well, using the sustaining pedal.

I know that for the purposes of your book it was necessary to attribute miraculous properties to this scene, but I think you go too far when you have David's mother *'spitting out a mouthful of wine'* and David's father *'fairly fainting at the sight of his angelic son's prodigality* (sic)'. David's parents were nothing if not rational, and they guessed immediately that this was one of Greta's practical jokes. Nothing in David's playing that day could have prepared them for the great leaps he would make during the next five years; for the moment they thought his feat merely cute, and finally irritating when he insisted on playing the same songs over and over again until well past his bedtime.

A piano teacher was duly called in, as you have written, *'to shepherd little David's talent up the steep and sometimes treacherous paths to true accomplishment.'* You might have added that David's parents hired this person (you do not identify him, but surely you remember that it was a young Jérôme Callois, who went on to disgrace himself so thoroughly during the 'political' *Evénements* of 1968?) not only to focus and channel David's playing as much as possible, but to exhaust the child at the keyboard before they returned home from work.

I simply cannot condone your use of such words as 'haunted' and 'wan' and 'eerily distracted' in your description of the very young David Debrizzi. This is too transparently a writer's foreshadowing. Elsewhere you use 'angelic', 'irresistible', and 'frankly beautiful', which are more like it. You know perfectly well, and have said so to me on many occasions including the first day we met in 1963, that David was the most adorable little boy either of us had ever seen. I cringed when I read your sentence about *'David's lush straight black hair parted in the middle, falling like Liszt's'*.

17

My God, Geoffrey, have you lost your mind? I will address your libellous physical descriptions of me in due course, but, honestly, all of this 'doe-eyed' and 'nacreous-skinned' rubbish is beyond the pale.

When I first met David he was five years old. I was nineteen. His parents had heard of me through the hateful Monsieur Presteron, who was responsible perhaps more than anyone else in this world for depriving me of the pianistic career that had been predicted for me by so many people. You tell this story well in your book, Geoffrey, I will give you that much. Even I had to laugh at your description of Presteron, the 'vile impresario' in his 'frock-like' clothes and his 'hideous, greasy moustache'. He was a villain, all right. What you omitted in your narrative was that Presteron charmed my parents, accepted their money for teaching and managing me, then rushed out to the cafés where he could gloat to his pseudo-Resistance friends that he had soaked a family of collaborators. It was Presteron who helped to fuel these rumours concerning my family's wartime activities, or lack of activities, which I was sorry to see recycled in your *Life*. Thank God my dear parents are dead and do not have to hear these warmed-over slanders from you, a man they truly liked.

Presteron was my fifth teacher. He took charge of me shortly after my sixteenth birthday, and took the fateful decision to launch my concert career when I had no business doing anything but warm-up scales in a soundproof basement. You will say I am being unduly modest, but I believe this to be the truth. At sixteen, like most prodigies, I had the technique of a master and the soul of a virgin.

It was Monsieur Presteron's idea that I should become famous for performing all of Rachmaninov's *Etudes-Tableaux*, at one sitting, exhibiting a technique far beyond my years. Perhaps he should be given credit for this notion, for he succeeded in establishing for me a reputation of ironclad technique and behemoth power at the keyboard. I was a large child, with unnaturally well-formed arms and hands. I played those works with my *back*, my friend. The recordings betrayed all of my weaknesses, though, and I would be surprised if anyone came to listen to me more than once. I must have been the only pianist in the world capable of one-thousand-per-cent dynamic changes alternating between semi-quavers. Where was Presteron, my supposed teacher, as I lashed out at the keyboard one moment, then slumped over for a feather touch, then ground out a deafening arpeggio, then softened to a whispery crawl – all of this governed by utter ignorance and a desire to please the sweating, coughing audience of the Salle Thierry? I will tell you where he was. He was backstage, counting money, and telling reporters that I was a difficult student, gloating over the strides he had made for me.

My only recollection of my last concert, refreshed by your book, is of my hands before me negotiating a monumental stretch, and of my imagining that my fingers were about to come apart at the webbing. I stopped playing. Monsieur Presteron hissed at me from the wings. I stared down at my hands as the audience made noises of embarrassment beyond the lights. I felt a swoon come over me as I tried to start again – I had been programmed to perform, after all. Out came the fingers. The audience went quiet. Down came the fingers, which still appeared alien and vulnerable to me. I listened for Rachmaninov and heard something quite different: Mozart, I am afraid. My fingers played the first piece I had ever performed in public, some six years previously. In that moment I hated all music. I ploughed through the Mozart gaudily, at treble tempo, added a few roulades for good measure, then slammed down the piano lid and rushed from the stage. The press reported this incident with typical mysticism, claiming that my genius had simply slipped the rails for a moment. Presteron tried to use this interpretation to his advantage, claiming I was possessed by Satan. Not true. I had never known such happiness, such freedom.

Your version of my movements after the concert is ever so slightly at variance with the facts. You have me wandering the streets of Paris in a state of confusion and despair, when actually I strolled down to the Deux Magots to enjoy a glass

19

of wine with Jean-Paul Sartre and his woman companion, where we discussed the effects of raw vegetables on the philosopher's bowels. I am at a loss as to why you have me visiting prostitutes on the night of my fateful last concert, when later on you inform your readers that I did not lose my virginity until the age of nineteen (in fact, I was thirteen, but this need not concern anyone).

I read your description of me as a sixteen year old with some concern:

> For three weeks following his disgrace at the Salle Thierry, he slumped through the nastier neighbour-hoods of his city like a great slug. Overweight since the age of five, and now bloated by premature addiction to wine and patisseries, this huge and hugely talented teenager lurched through the streets, a completely aimless ne'er-do-well.

Do slugs slump and lurch? How can you write these words when your own book contains photographs of me looking nothing if not fit and distinguished? Big, yes, but not unpleasant to look at, I wouldn't have thought, and never *completely* aimless. In real life I stayed home and played the piano quite beautifully, and revelled in the realization that I would never have to play in public again. Monsieur Presteron sued my parents for breach of contract, and won.

Even as wicked a man as Monsieur Presteron has his compassionate moments, so perhaps it was because he felt sorry for me that he arranged for my interview with David Debrizzi's parents. It took him three years to find this outlet for his generosity – a time I spent not, as you have it, '*flouncing about the seedier areas in search of mean-ing between the thighs* of filles de joie', but passing my Bac in the hope of finding a career beyond the piano. I went to the interview with every intention of turning down any offer the Debrizzis might make; in other words, I was unprepared for the effect little David would have on me.

20

'Whatever you do,' Madame Debrizzi said to me, on that cool April morning, 'don't play chess with him.'

Now as you have experienced first hand, Geoffrey, I am something of a wizard at the chess board. A substantial portion of my teenage income came from café chess games with a group of acquaintances whose fortunes were greater than their skill.

'Oh, David plays chess, does he?' I said to Madame Debrizzi.

'My husband taught him, or rather unleashed him, about a year ago.'

'I play a bit,' I said, blowing on my fingertips. 'A quick game might just break the ice.'

Madame Debrizzi sighed wearily. 'He will only toy with you,' she said. She led me from the kitchen, where we had met to confer out of David's hearing, into the 'piano room'.

I liked Camille Debrizzi, but then I am always drawn to large women with intelligent faces. Even when David was only five, Camille had that puffy, exhausted look that would become ever more pronounced, roughly in proportion to the demands David made on her time and patience. It was the face of an excellent, dedicated teacher. (By the way, your description of Camille's job makes her sound like a charwoman; I suppose from your lofty social perspective almost everyone exists at that level.) So many parents panic when their children exhibit extraordinary ability, but Camille took it all in her tired stride

'Is that David playing now?' I asked, as we walked down the hallway. The strains of some rather overheated Beethoven had been audible throughout our conversation in the kitchen.

'Either that,' said Camille, 'or his grandmother has had some sort of epiphany.'

'Oh, my,' I said. 'It sounds awfully good.'

You might assume – in fact, you *did* assume, in that incoherent page-and-a-half describing my first meeting with David – that as a former child prodigy myself I would not be overawed by David's playing. I cannot tell you how wrong you are. Even Camille, who had given birth to this prodigy,

21

nursed him, reared him, and heard him play perhaps more than she would have liked, seemed to gasp and sway when we entered the piano room. David was so *small*, and the music he played was so *big*.

I was struck by the eerie impression that David's little arms were so thin, his hands so delicate, that it seemed impossible for him to depress a single key even with his full weight behind the effort. And yet there he sat (he was tall enough to sit by then, although an attachment had been made so that he could reach the sustaining pedal), grinding out the mightier passages of batty Ludwig's last piano sonata. When he noticed us in the doorway he stopped playing in the middle of a theme, and swivelled round on the bench to say hello. You do go on a bit about the boy's beauty, but I agree that it would be hard to convey without repetition. He was an angel. Even his mother seemed to go weak at the sight of him, piano or no piano.

'Do you know how to play chess?' he asked me.

'Yes, as a matter of fact I do.'

'Shall we play a game?'

'What a good idea, David.'

Camille's body did exactly what your language says it should: it heaved a sigh.

David hopped off his piano bench and made for a chess board set on a low table on the other side of the room. Its pieces formed, I noticed, the frozen aftermath of slaughter for his side.

'I want you to be whichever colour you like,' said David, rearranging the pieces.

'I'll be black, then,' I said. I removed my jacket and asked permission to smoke. I rolled up my sleeves as David turned the board around and moved pawn to king four.

'I'll bring coffee,' said Camille, with another sigh. 'If it takes that long.'

Not all great pianists are great chess players, and vice versa, but I would hazard a guess that this is merely due to lack of time to practise both disciplines. I know that in my case, after my . . . my *retirement*, when I devoted more of my cerebral energies to chess, that my game seemed to feed off the energy I no longer expended memorizing music at the keyboard. And David, five-year-old David, who had these talents to spare and little else to do with his time – well, David could really play chess.

By the time Camille returned with coffee I had loosened my tie, smoked three cigarettes, and become embroiled in a middle game of such awesome complexity that it was all I could do to feign good cheer when I accepted my cup. For the first eight moves I had optimistically assumed that little David Debrizzi was playing along with the book version of my transposed opening because he had chanced to see it in a recent game. I expected him to lose his way when I added my oft-tested deviation. I was heartened when David crossed his legs and gave my unusual move some consideration; his other moves had not seemed to occupy his mind at all – in fact he had occasionally browsed through one of his hardbound sheet-music books while I mulled over my own strategy. I would soon realize he had been memorizing the score. Needless to say, for his prowess at the chess board has since become legendary – though not helped by your dismissal of his game as 'notoriously reckless' – David promptly dissected my offence in ten moves, and on move twenty-eight, down a bishop to a pawn, I suggested he might like to play the piano for me.

Before going to the piano David shook my hand – he made that stunningly adult eye-contact – and said, 'Thank you for one of the best games ever.'

I am sure you are quite correct when you write that David's parents selected me, via Monsieur Presteron, more for my social contacts than for my qualifications as a teacher of advanced children. But with all due modesty I think I can add that my then notorious collapse, well argued among connoisseurs of prodigies, must have given them the hope that I of all people could steer David clear of such a fate. Musical and scientific journals had written about my condition. A syndrome had been named after me, in fruitless expectation of further examples. (You were wise not to go into this arcane subject in your book, but did you have to dismiss my retirement from the stage as 'a moral collapse', and 'psychosomatic arthritic seizure'? That's pap journalism. When a teenager goes on stage intending to play Rachmaninov and retreats with visions of his wrists exploding in tsunamis of blood on to the keys, he has every reason to be wary of continuing.)

Bruised by my defeat at the chess board, I stood by the piano and watched with as serene an expression as I could muster while David went through his pianistic paces for me. I wanted him to sight-read something, if only to discover a chink in his armour, but there was not a scrap of music in the room that he had not already memorized.

When David had finished showing off, I asked him if he would like me to return for formal coaching. He nodded and smiled, said 'We could play more chess,' then launched into another piece. I searched out his mother, who was cooking and chatting with her mother-in-law, and told her I would be happy to teach her son. I knew that any negotiation of my fee would be in bad taste, given the state of the Debrizzi finances and my family's well-publicized prosperity, so we quickly settled on a nominal weekly sum with the understanding that I would always arrive bearing edible gifts. I went back into the piano room to say goodbye to David, but could not bring myself to interrupt his gentle rendition of one of Schumann's *Intermezzi*.

I am getting carried away by detail, when my sole purpose is to attack the meat of your biography. This will not take long. A few more points, then, before moving along to your Chapter Two.

> *In the hands of his new and rather immature teacher, David seemed to grow bored with music. He veered off into the kind of musical escapism that would result in the vulgar parodies of Chopin he often played for me.*

Am I to take the blame for David's playful streak? It was all I could do to get him to play a piano piece in the proper key. Let's be honest, Geoffrey: there has never, ever, been a child of David's transpositional fluency. It is your adult prejudice that sees his careering off into foreign keys as unmusical and disrespectful. The truth is that he didn't give a damn about music at that age, any more than he would have cared about orthodox chess openings – just so long as he won.

David told me he practised two to three hours every day, but I suspect he played far longer. When I first began to work with him it was for one hour, three times a week – not the live-in nanny role depicted in your biography. With both of his parents at work and his grandmother in need of peace and quiet, our lessons usually involved nothing more than a quick game of chess – in which I would be quietly but ruthlessly put down like a rabid dog – and a chat about the music David had digested during the previous forty-eight hours. He was going through a sponge-like phase of learning and experimentation. I am quite certain that his parents' only requirement of me was to alert them to the signs of madness they seemed to believe must invariably accompany such a musical 'gift'. I watched him closely and detected no signs of imbalance, unless you include a certain sadism displayed at the chess board.

David's father Henri worked as a printer, an occupation you seem to have mentioned only because it allowed you to identify the capacity in which Henri managed *not* to betray humanity to the Nazis. I am trying to imagine you in your study at Dollsworthy as you wrote or typed or dictated that paragraph about David's father's wartime behaviour. Clichés have never bothered you, I know, but if you were going to write all of that nonsense about jackboots ringing out on cobblestones, why not go all the way back to the 'storm clouds gathering over Europe' – or perhaps you had used that phrase in a previous book. Then again, I always had difficulty thinking metaphorically.

The jackboots rang out on Parisian cobblestones. French printing shops all too eagerly banged out the posters that today, frayed and jaundiced, adorn the walls of mankind's museums of evil.

By pointing out that we have no proof of Henri's having contributed to this immoral madness, you elevate him nearly to the level of hero.

My family does not escape so easily. You do your best to drag our name into the ranks of infamy, based on what my father may have done or not done to stem or abet the 'tide of evil' (for God's sake). Even I am a victim of your blanket indictment, though I was not born until rather late on in 1942. Perhaps you believe that my father's ability to conceive a child during the Occupation is sufficient proof of his living the good life, *'while all around him Hitler's butchers plied their grisly trade'*, etc. It is true that the Nazis were invariably cordial to my family, but I hope we can say that the reverse was not always true. I suppose I am not surprised that you believe in hereditary guilt, when I have seen you get so much mileage out of your grandfather's posthumous VC.

Most Frenchmen, you will have noticed, tend to keep fairly mum on the subject of collaboration, whether or not they behaved sufficiently heroically – or suicidally – to gain an Englishman's approval. The idea your book promotes is that in order to have behaved even remotely well during the Occupation, an individual would now have to be commemorated on one of the quaint plaques screwed into Parisian walls here and there: *Ici est tombé . . .* Would that do the trick?

Having neatly traduced my household – and exonerated David's – you rush to the end of your Chapter One so that your favourite personal pronoun can re-enter the narrative. You leave the reader fearing that young David has fallen into the clutches of a pack of mad Nazis bent on his destruction. And do not think for a moment that I missed the paedophiliac innuendo in your description of my 'doting'

26

on my 'beloved' David. You could just as easily have written about my brief marital engagement, but then you would have risked boring your devoted fans. I suppose the story of Jacqueline's dying in my arms pales in comparison to a mere hint of child molesting.

Your CHAPTER TWO

I returned to David Debrizzi's life shortly after his ninth birthday, fresh from a rather tedious two years discovering that I was ill-suited to a career in politics. Never again would I stray from music and writing.

This false modesty will be lost only on the few who fail to glance at the jacket of your book, which informs us that at the age of thirty-one you nearly unseated a cabinet minister. Would that you had, Geoffrey. Think of all David and I might have been spared.

At last I make my formal entrance on to the stage of your *Life*:

Pierre Marie La Valoise – burly and dishevelled, well over six feet tall, moving nervously for a man his size . . . his great arms and hands like sledgehammers . . . an enormous appetite for wine . . . eccentric clothing . . . a gloomy cast to his features owing perhaps to the fantastic disappointment of a concert career cut short . . . never sitting still . . . full of news of David's improvement . . . proud as a new father.

All of this by way of contrast to you, Geoffrey. What an elegant figure you cut when we met at my father's house (*'a humble café'*?); and sat out on the lawn in the sweet spring breeze (*'rancid coffee in a haze of Gauloise smoke'*?); watching my father's gardeners work their topiary wonders (*'speaking over the grumbling after-work conversation of red-nosed labourers'*?). I suppose to point out that my father was a not-wholly-landless baron and a captain of industry would have thrown off your subtly constructed aura of superiority to these amusing little French people.

You give every impression that David's playing 'improved' – that is to say took off like a rocket, to the point where we had to turn down exploitative, freak-show concert invitations from five countries a week – not thanks to, but *despite* my influence. Much as I admired you, I could not help being offended at the manner in which you set about taking charge of David's 'trajectory', as you have it, without asking my permission.

Your self-confidence was impressive, and understandable, but I questioned your motives. Why, I asked myself, would such an accomplished music man – there is no single word for what you were: amateur pianist, conductor, composer, critic, patron, diner at the tables of maestros – waste his time on the instruction of an unproven child? Much as I would like to plumb your Freudian depths over this matter – and I have learned quite a lot of jargon from your mind-mining passages on David – I can only solve this puzzle with the obvious: you needed a genius protégé to bolster your image at the creative end of your musical and social lives. It would be convenient to turn the tables and accuse you of being infatuated with David, but despite your harrowing early education I have never been able to think of you as a paedophile, strictly speaking. You knew David would make a splash, and you wanted to dive in with him.

In those days, insecure as I must have been, I felt less anger at your intrusion than simple relief when you agreed to keep me on as David's 'daily' teacher, and the money you sent his parents did not go amiss.

David's skill had ripened during my absence. He was less playful at the keyboard, more respectful of his instrument. I was pleased to see that he had developed a sensitive outlook and a vocabulary that gave vent to verbal, rather than merely digital, interpretation of the more abstract facets of the music we loved.

I am afraid I could not be so pleased with his then tutor, Pierre Marie La Valoise. I considered him a dangerous influence, and found it hard to understand why David's parents had kept him on as long as they had. Everything I learned about his spectacular failure six or seven years before compounded my distrust of this rather unkempt and unreliable figure. Our reunion in Paris made matters worse, when I saw to what extent La Valoise had fallen into loose living and moral decay.

Would you be referring to Gretchen and Hilda, by any chance? Geoffrey, I am deeply wounded. My rational side tells me you only write these words in order later to lay blame at my door for David's future amorous distractions, because I simply cannot believe that your discovery of my multiple dalliance alone could lead you to state that I was 'depraved'. I was merely in the throes of the first stages of mourning for my late fiancée Jacqueline, and you should have recognized that.

I can see you now, in my Paris house, come to offer me the job I already held: hand extended in greeting, sumptuous tweed, curiosity in your eyes as you took in the unexpected splendour of my home, and then the shock when Gretchen and Hilda pranced into the drawing room reeking, to your nostrils, of immorality.

'My word,' you kept repeating. 'My *word.*' Here, you must have thought, is one of those Froggy troilists.

I have a sneaking suspicion – and it must have occurred to me all those years ago – that you were sexually inexperienced to, shall we say, an infinite degree. I know this can happen in England. What would not have occurred to me then was that you might actually disapprove of my ménage. I was terribly happy with it – or as happy as a man can be when he is in perpetual mourning. If it makes you feel any better, Gretchen and Hilda were sisters.

'My *word*,' you said, yet again. You admired my piano and asked if I still played. I said 'Not really,' in a way you surely understood to mean the contrary. You could not peel your eyes away from Gretchen and Hilda, who were, yes, *German*, perhaps rehearsing in your mind what you would write a quarter of a century later regarding the collaborationist tendencies of my family.

We marched out into fine weather and chatted superficially on the way to David's house. This was 1965, a splendid year for those of us who kept an eye on politics. We discussed the coming presidential election, to which I was opposed – I was opposed to elections in general in those days. I had rather counted on De Gaulle's crowning himself emperor before the year's end. (In the event, my family survived democracy.) You were in a less than buoyant mood, as I recall, having so recently attended Sir Winston Churchill's funeral. I notice that you mention this historic landmark, just in case we forgot how well connected you were, amid a generous amount of other period detail. Your efforts at verisimilitude only make your interpretive errors more jarring to the well-informed reader.

In hindsight I understand that you were horrified by me, and by my household arrangement. At the time I was oblivious of your disapproval, happy just to be strolling along with an angry young lion, or whatever you fancied yourself to be. My 'breakdown', as you insist upon calling it, had done nothing to diminish my enthusiasm for music – for its practitioners and patrons alike. Now I knew both. I thought that if everything went well I would have a new family: David, a friend and a convenient replacement for my lost musical life; and Geoffrey, my much admired mentor. I thought even Gretchen and Hilda might fit in, or their equivalents. I was as happy as a man with a dead spot in his heart can possibly be.

David met us at the door of the courtyard that led to his parents' house, still wearing his school uniform. He shook hands with you in his adult way, then greeted me with the hug that had replaced the kiss – and that he would abandon in its turn three years later in favour of a more manful meeting of the eyes.

'Do you remember Mr Flynch?' I remember asking him, as we climbed the stairs.

'The assassination man,' said David.

'That's right,' I said. 'Well done.'

You looked puzzled by this, until I reminded you of the date of your first encounter with David.

We sat in the piano room and were served coffee by Greta, David's *grandmother*.

'Mr Flynch has been talking to your parents,' I explained to David, who sat on the piano bench with his back to the keyboard, facing a scene of ruination on the chess board. 'They think he would be a useful teacher for you. Not teacher, really, am I right, Mr Flynch? Master classes, is what we are discussing. A broad range of coaching and management.'

David narrowed his eyes at me. 'You don't want to teach me any more?'

'Nothing of the kind. I am told I will be able to continue working with you as always. It is simply that Mr Flynch will–'

'Let me explain,' you interrupted, in French. 'There comes a time when all kinds of considerations must be balanced against the normal continuation . . .' (this sentence David would have understood as 'considerations *thrown* against') '. . . of your education outside music.'

David covered his mouth and giggled. 'I don't quite understand you,' he said, in perfect English. 'You could try in your own language.'

Remember, Geoffrey, that David liked games. One little game he and I had played together for the past four years was called 'Speaking English Together All The Time'. My American step-mother had done the same with me, and it has proved infinitely valuable. David was fluent even then, although in your Chapter Four you take full credit for his linguistic accomplishments. No doubt that is why this important conversation does not appear in your book.

You repeated your case for a fuller immersion in the piano, and a carefully planned dip of the toe into public performance.

'Why are you frowning, David?' you asked him.

David rubbed his bare knees with his magical hands. He looked at me as if asking my permission to speak his mind. With my eyes I indicated that he should go ahead.

'Mr Flynch, when would be the first time I had to play?'

'Well, now, that is to say, not if you, it's really quite a . . . do you mean to tell me that you've never. . .?'

'I thought surely you knew,' I said. 'David's reputation rests entirely on home-made recordings, including the ones you have heard.'

You looked as if you were about to accuse little David of fraud, but held your tongue in time. 'I see,' you said instead. 'A bit wary of the stage, then, are you, my boy?'

'I think so,' said David. 'Yes.'

Oh, how well I knew what you were thinking as you turned and glowered at me. You were thinking I had brainwashed David into suffering from my own 'stage fright', if that is what you call what a man has when he dissolves into hallucinations when performing in public. It is true that I usually counselled against a recital, but never, ever, did I suggest to David that this was something to be feared. I simply never saw any purpose in parading a boy in front of perfect strangers. There would be plenty of time for that. But no, there it is in your Chapter Two: '*It could not have been more obvious to me that La Valoise had already instilled in David Debrizzi a terror of the stage that would take months or even years to overcome.*'

Did I do *nothing* right in all that time?

'No need to rush things,' you said, reaching over to pat one of David's hands. 'We'll have a little word with your parents.'

The way this part of David's life reads in your book, you simply swept into Paris, scooped him up, and popped him down on the stage of the Salle Thierry, the very hall that had witnessed my final, aborted concert. In fact, as you know perfectly well, a stormy year intervened.

Given what went on, I find it entirely understandable that you omitted that year, and cut directly to David's first concert under your 'management'. To this day I am not sure how much of the truth you know, so for old times' sake let me enlighten you.

David soon established to your satisfaction that he was no fraud, that he could play everything I said he could, that his recordings were authentic. With David's credentials certified, you set out to remove me from the scene. In your position I might have done the same thing, but your methods were crude and devious, and based on the disgust you felt as a result of glimpsing behind the doors of my private life.

For two or three months you bided your time, you plotted, you connived. Your methods smacked of public school pranks. You took up a residence four blocks closer to David's house than mine. Your reputation in Britain seemed to benefit from your absence. You began to research your (awful and award-winning) biography, *Foray into Fauré*, which was the ostensible purpose of your stay in Paris. You pretended to befriend me. You even pretended to befriend Gretchen and Hilda – who soon were transformed before your eyes into Anita and Gabrielle, though you did not appear to notice the difference. Your lip curled each time you met them.

Think back, Geoffrey, think back. Try to remember how you behaved, what you looked like, what thoughts crossed your youngish mind. What, I ask myself now, could it have felt like to live inside the mind and body of a possibly virgin thirty-two year old? I have no proof, of course, only the circumstantial evidence of your behaviour in the company of girls. But if I lacked scruples – that is to say if I were more like you – my *Death of David Debrizzi* would have included colourful passages enunciating my theory of your sexual inexperience, or rather non-experience. I would, unfairly, have chalked it up to your being English – much the way you found my terribly unusual and in all ways satisfactory style of life merely 'French'. But I have explained it to myself in the standard way: your early life was a continuum of all-male institutions from the moment you left your nanny's arms. You emerged petrified. What a way, I say to myself aloud, for a young musician to live.

Your plan was to defame me in the eyes of David's parents by exposing them to what you considered to be my sordid domestic arrangement. This you set out to achieve by planning to meet me for a drink at my house, and, without telling me, inviting all three Debrizzis. You were going to pretend to have forgotten to tell me about this aspect of our evening. 'Are you *quite sure* I didn't mention them?' you were going to say.

I do not doubt that Henri and Camille would have been surprised to see the way I lived, if your plan had come off as you had hoped – not because they would have disapproved of a young man with a large house having friends come to stay, but because they probably never realized until then that I lived in such a palatial residence. Whether they would have dropped me as David's teacher and companion is another question; as you never fail to mention, you were dealing with unpredictably liberal French folk. But we would never know, for your plot was unwittingly leaked to me by David himself.

Not normally a vindictive man, I nevertheless decided that pre-emptive retaliation was in order. Anita and Gabrielle and I put our heads together and settled on what we thought was a clever turning of the tables. The girls were intrigued by my theory concerning your virginity, and took this possibility as the catalyst of our scheme. I must give credit where credit is due, and say that Anita and Gabrielle were mainly responsible for what happened. They were vicious, where I was merely spiteful. Also I am sure they considered any matter of seduction to be an irresistible challenge. I did not have to egg them on, in other words. I simply provided the venue – my house – and the phone call to the Debrizzis changing the date of the rendezvous you had planned with them. I wanted their visit to follow yours by some fifteen hours. The girls assured me you would still be around. A rather large wager was attached to this prediction, I might add.

They were lovely girls, weren't they, Geoffrey? Anita, so dark and big and jolly. Really, she was wonderful. There was so *much* of Anita. And while there was a good deal less of Gabrielle, what there was of her one could not have improved upon. You remember, Geoffrey, surely? Gabrielle: the one with the enormous mouth and the contagious laughter and a physical love of Chopin? I used to arrange piano music for six hands. We would pull the love seat up to the piano and play together, all three, me in the middle. Yes, they were lovely girls; I remember them fondly.

What your memory of them is I would not presume to say, except that you must have expended a great deal of psychic energy over the years trying to block them out, the little devils. You arrived at my house at the appointed hour, bearing chocolates for the girls and a bottle of wine for me. You were, I know, buttering us up. Of course I insisted that we drink the wine straightaway. For all your references to my immoderate consumption of wine, I must say for the record that you were no mean imbiber yourself in those days.

Along with the wine, you swallowed your disapproval of Anita and Gabrielle, and discussed David's prospects with me in their presence. You listened politely when Anita insisted on 'auditioning' for you. Gabrielle put on an act of shyness, waiting for you to beg her to play. You remember the room: a vast marble hall, the Bösendorfer starkly black against the white columns and nymphs, the unlimited supply of food and drink transported by one or other of the girls on castor-wheeled serving tables. I am not ashamed to say that I lived very well indeed.

You became relaxed and expansive. We spoke of music and other pleasant topics. You glanced surreptitiously at your watch every few minutes, wondering when the Debrizzis would make their untimely entrance and discover the truth about my behaviour behind closed doors. You seemed quite encouraged about the likely success of your plot when the girls returned from elsewhere in my house wearing alluring costumes: Anita, all of Anita, in full belly-dancing regalia, including a genuine emerald in her navel; and Gabrielle, sweet Gabrielle, in her eunuch's pyjamas, her slight bosom tightly wrapped, a submissive posture to her shoulders, a downcast look in her eyes.

I activated the record player. Anita danced and cling-clanged her finger-cymbals. Gabrielle stood next to where we sat, fanning us with an enormous palm frond that had been sent to her by a Lebanese brother-in-law. I could tell you were now torn between wanting the Debrizzis to arrive at once so that they would burst in on this particularly colourful scene, and wanting the show to continue uninterrupted for your own enjoyment. Anita's bare feet clapped on the marble as she gyrated her lavish flesh. Gabrielle remained expressionless and servile. I kept the wine flowing.

I had known these girls for some months. We were a happy family by that time. Gretchen and Hilda were a pleasant – if quite familiar – memory. We went everywhere together, and did not experience disagreement or friction of any sort. A ménage you had diagnosed as immoral and destructive was, you soon discovered, really rather a lot of fun. This realization crept over you – even as you continued to peek at your watch – until you were comfortable enough to accept the pre-wrapped turban Gabrielle placed on your head, and to remark to me that so far you found the evening 'jolly interesting'.

You will forgive me for trying to analyze your sexual foibles, but I feel justified in doing so because you felt compelled to foist your half-baked theories about David and me on the British reading public. It is my belief that you had grown into adulthood and several years beyond with the firm conviction that sexual intercourse was something men often wanted, but which women put on a par with, say, amoebic dysentery. It would have shocked you, I know, to have discovered that both Anita and Gabrielle were thrilled by the idea of going to bed with you – I had rather built you up, I have to admit – so much so that they had become a shade competitive on the subject. It was a pleasure for me to watch conflicting emotions playing across your face as you realized the evening had been organized for your benefit. Anita drew nearer to you, inexpert at belly-dancing, but ever so enticing. Gabrielle, handicapped by her constricting costume, played up her boyishness and seemed to gain the upper hand.

I sensed victory for Gabrielle when she began to feed you peeled grapes. She peeled them with her teeth, slowly, as Anita squinted at her from behind her gold-speckled veil, and fed them to you one by one with her long, masculine fingers. Her huge mouth, when not employed peeling grapes, was a frozen line of concentration and obedience.

'Wouldn't you like Gabrielle to sit on your lap?' I asked you, uncorking brandy.

'Oh, she needn't . . . it would be . . . yes, please.'

To Anita's chagrin, Gabrielle installed herself chastely on your knees. You gulped at the brandy and did not unstick your gaze from Gabrielle's peachy neck. Anita danced down the centre of the room and made her disappointed exit, only to return two minutes later wearing one of my dress shirts and nothing more.

Goodness, you were drunk and lustful. You were satisfied that the Debrizzis would not be arriving so late, that there must have been a mix-up. You screwed up your courage and stroked the hackles on the nape of Gabrielle's neck. Your tie seemed to loosen itself of its own accord.

Anita and I installed ourselves at the piano and played – do you remember? – my own transcription for two hands of the Tannhäuser Overture. Anita always enjoyed playing the lower register, leaving the gaudy violin parts to me. Her great, heavy arms pounded out the brass theme as her hair fell on to sweaty cheeks. We executed a final, mighty crescendo with some flair, and a great deal of moaning on Anita's part, and turned around, expecting applause.

What a sight you were, Geoffrey. Gabrielle's hands were clasped around your head as she administered one of her apocalyptic kisses, for which she was born, her eyes screwed shut in intense concentration. You, on the other hand, looked

38

like a victim of the electric chair: arms and legs flung out in mid air, eye-whites prominent, hair standing on end at the sides of your glorious turban. You had no way of knowing that Gabrielle's kiss had only just begun. Gabrielle, her mouth a dedicated kissing organ, would happily have continued in this vein for two hours before thinking of repositioning her nose *vis-à-vis* yours. It gives me pleasure to recall this scene for you, not because I hope to remind you of it, but because I know a day has probably not gone by, a kiss has not been kissed, without your knees going weak at the recollection. Gabrielle's kissing was one of the reasons I married her two years later.

Anita and I launched into another piece, a softer one more suited to the mood on the other side of the room. We watched over our shoulders as your legs slowly descended to the floor and your arms inexorably wrapped around the slender back of Gabrielle. I wondered to myself if it were possible that you had never kissed a woman before.

Anita put a brave face on her defeat. She whispered a vow that she would do her best to follow quickly on Gabrielle's heels. Anita was not so accomplished a kisser as her younger friend, but, my God, there was a great deal of Anita.

By midnight the lights had been turned low, David's own recordings were being played, Anita and I were sprawled on pillows behind the piano, and Gabrielle had inserted one excruciatingly delicate finger between the buttons of your shirt, her kissing unabated. You were transported, first spiritually, then physically: Gabrielle led you by the hand into one of the guest bedrooms and slammed the door shut. Anita and I repaired to the master bedroom, where we made love to the clickety-clack of a film projector showing – quite rare in those days – African anthropology films. At three in the morning, after hearing Gabrielle's astonishing cries of release through the wall, Anita bathed, then stole into your room on silent feet.

I would not dare speculate as to what went on in there for the next eight hours, and both Anita and Gabrielle were uncharacteristically reticent on the matter when I asked them for details. What is of historical record is that Henri, Camille and David Debrizzi arrived the next morning, as planned, to find me in the kitchen preparing coffee, and to see you stumble out of my guest room wearing only a turban and an expression of utter bewilderment, followed by two giggling and strangely attired young ladies.

David scurried to the piano and began to play impatient warm-up scales. Henri and Camille nodded hello to you, a greeting you reciprocated with over-trained formality before fleeing to the bedroom for your clothes. When you joined us five minutes later you had concealed every part of your body save for your trembling hands and your blood-flushed cheeks. You found Henri and Camille chatting amicably with Anita and Gabrielle; you searched their faces for signs of disapproval and, finding none, trained your eyes on me. When the double-cross dawned on you – which took some time; you had a great deal to take in, and a splitting brandy headache on top – you attempted a glare in my direction, but could finally manage only a look of grudging respect, tinged with gratitude.

You hardly seemed to listen as our little meeting ratified me as David's principal teacher, you as his 'guiding spirit' and financier. You did a good deal of bowing. You had only kind words to say about me, even if they were delivered with some hysteria. David, you assured his parents, could not be in better hands than mine. The girls had gone over to watch David play his scales, to marvel at his supreme cuteness, and in their demeanour to give an overall impression of the previous night's debauchery. The Debrizzis said their goodbyes, prising David from the piano, without showing a trace of the misgivings you had presumed they would have – for which, under the circumstances, you were quite grateful.

I do hope I did nothing that morning to capitalize further on my small triumph. I felt quite warmly towards you, all in all, but in a curious way I felt that I was now your equal. I tried to put myself in your position. It awed me to contemplate how much had happened to you, so suddenly, thanks to me and my girls.

I invited you to join me and the girls for lunch, but you declined, saying you wanted to go home 'for a think'. I did not speak to you for three or four days, until you rang to ask me to dinner. We met at Le Telephone, and I sensed from the outset that your 'think' had been arduous, but conclusive. What were the chances, you wanted to know, of seeing Gabrielle or Anita, or both, again? Very high, I said, seeing that they lived in my house. Yes, you agreed, but what about, what about, what were the chances of recreating our night of dressing up and frolicking? I said you would have to ask Gabrielle and Anita. And what if, you continued, what if, if Gabrielle and Anita were too attached to me, say, what might, what about the chances of my finding another girl to pursue similar activities in your recently changed life?

Thus Louise.

I don't know if I ever told you where I met Louise. Your first suspicion was that I had become acquainted with her during one of my 'psychopathic skulkings' up and down the Rue St Denis – figments of your imagination that play a prominent part in nearly all your published descriptions of my life a quarter of a century ago. When I told you she was English, your face fell; you reminded me obliquely of the services you expected from whatever matchmaking it might be possible for me to arrange. I assured you that Louise, after years spent roaming Europe and North Africa with a copy of *L'Etranger* under her arm, was likely to be worth a surprise or two.

It will be news to you that I first met Louise in London in 1958, where I had travelled in the company of my father. We were thrilled, despite ourselves, to accept an invitation to dine with your adorable young Queen, who took to my father in the strongest way, and who remembered to wish me a royal happy sixteenth birthday. I recall this benediction not so much because it was Queen Elizabeth who uttered it, but because standing behind her, gorgeous and aloof, was a girl my age before whom God had clearly intended me to throw down the gauntlet of love. This I managed to do after

41

extricating myself from a most sincere conversation with Her Majesty, sprinting outside, and reaching my beloved's car in time to fling myself headlong into its path. The driver was not amused, and without his young passenger's intervention might have encouraged the guards, who were even then converging on the scene, to cart me away to the Tower. Lying on the gravel in my evening clothes, I looked up into the face of Louise, which was silhouetted by a moon-silvered fog. I announced my love for her in the presence of her parents, her driver, and half a dozen flustered soldiers.

Louise liked me immediately. Over the protestations of her parents, we exchanged coordinates.

Louise's father, Lord Fisch, was a scowling, prematurely bejowled old fool - perhaps you knew him? He was just well enough in touch with the reality beyond the walls of his estate to know that without the tightest security his daughter was likely to be swept up in what promised to be a rebellious decade.

He was too late. At our first meeting Louise confessed to me, during one of the short breaks when our lips were not entwined, that she had already arranged a pilgrimage to India - obligatory in those days – for the coming spring. She invited me to join her there, and I accepted. Our secret plans had to be shelved when Monsieur Presteron took charge of me a few weeks later and insisted that I begin a rigorous schedule of doomed public performances. Needless to say, Louise found a substitute companion, trudged off to India, and achieved her combined aims of broadening her horizons, indulging in unchaperoned love-making, and annoying her father to the verge of a nervous breakdown. She returned to London tanned, eighteen, Buddhist and pregnant.

Pausing in England only long enough to shame her father by asking all his friends if they knew a reliable abortionist, Louise packed up her rucksack and sitar and fled to France in search of Albert Camus, who was killed two days before she was to be introduced to him. Her mourning took the form of two years' traipsing about Camus' haunts in an existential trance. She returned to Paris tanned, twenty, Moslem and pregnant.

Louise moved in with me – and one other girlfriend – and consulted a doctor friend of mine. She did much to help me through the first stages of my mourning Jacqueline's death. Louise was still young and lovely, but our religions were incompatible and what might have been was not. She moved away, making room for Gretchen and Hilda, but we kept in touch.

It surprises me now that her name sprang first to mind when you requested my matchmaking services at Le Telephone. I suppose I continued to hold you, or your dubious accomplishments, in high esteem. Louise was far and away the most challenging English-speaking girl in my big black book, so we must assume that I either thought you up to the task, or I hoped the encounter would leave you broken and humiliated. I could see that you were anxious about the meeting, and you kept asking me where and when it would take place. Impulsive as always, I strode to the bar at Le Telephone, where indeed they had a telephone, and called Louise. I came back to the table and said 'She'll be right here,' and saw you jerk your hands to your thinning hair to organize a more presentable Geoffrey.

Louise's entrance did not disappoint. She wore the seductive look of impatient distraction that only very privileged girls can carry off, looking not at the faces of the clientele but at the ceiling fan, as if a clue to her whereabouts might be derived from its wobbly revolutions. Imagine how wonderful Louise must have been in North Africa, landing in coffee houses with her nose in the air and a banned paperback in her hand – how innocent, how inspiring, how *preyed-upon*. Recent sunny travels had freckled her face. Primitive jewellery and an exotic handbag advertised her satisfied wanderlust. I had to walk across the room and kiss her four times before she noticed I was in the restaurant.

You will remember how you were smitten by Louise. I suppose I would have predicted that your reaction to meeting such an electrifying person would have been a kind

43

of panicked silence, or a desperately improvised feigning of superiority. I would not have guessed that you would suddenly attempt to reverse centuries of breeding by trying to portray yourself as a dissipated émigré/artiste to whom opiates and free love came as second nature.

You loosened your tie and ordered French cigarettes and generally gutted your accent. You employed foul language, heaped abuse on your erstwhile friends, scoffed at those who had called you merely brilliant. Louise smoked and drank and looked lovely and was so unfazed by what you had to say that it only inflamed you, and sent you soaring to such heights of bad taste that several hundred deceased Flynches must have rolled simultaneously in their crypts of Albion.

Louise's ingrained good manners had not been eroded by her forays into barbarous lands. She suffered you gladly. She sat close to you. Her light and delicate eyebrows danced with amusement at the self-aggrandizing stories you told. As the younger man I allowed you to hold forth, not knowing that you would do so at a succession of increasingly *risqué caves*, until dawn. I could not recognize the man I had taken for a virgin only a few days before, and who had been first shocked, then seduced, by the playful behaviour of my live-in friends.

To my even greater surprise, Louise seemed enchanted by the new you. She remained uncharacteristically silent, hung on your tortured mix of truth and fiction, reciprocated the frequent physical contact that you, unbelievably, initiated. I left you waltzing away into the misty morn by the Seine, remarking to myself that in five years living independently in Paris this was the first time someone had gone on revelling longer than I.

Within a fortnight you asked Louise to marry you. Her refusal was the first tragedy to encroach on your otherwise charmed life. When she could not give you concrete reasons for turning you down, you came to me for an explanation. You told me to give it to you straight: if you were despicable, you wanted to know why. You swallowed your pride and asked a younger man – however much more experienced –

for advice. You stood at attention in my drawing room like a junior officer informed of imminent court martial. Your upper lip could not have been stiffer. I hesitated to answer your questions, for I did not want to precipitate a suicide.

'Without decoration,' you said, from behind a quivering chin. 'I wish to know the truth.'

'A drink first?' I suggested, stalling.

'It is clear to me from your expression that you know something you are not telling me. Why, I ask you again, has Louise rejected my proposal?'

'Must we be so formal, Geoffrey? You could sit down, at least.'

'No, thank you. I wish to know the truth.'

'Louise said nothing?'

'Nothing by way of explanation.'

I remember that I stood up and put my hand on your shoulder – a gesture that would have been unthinkable a week before. I suppose it helped that physically I dwarfed you.

'I want to make sure you take what I have to say the right way,' I said. My improvisation could have used polishing. 'My English, as you know, is not what it should be.' This transparent untruth you no doubt believed, in self-defence.

'Go on,' you said, standing straighter and raising your jaw.

'I have spoken to Louise since your . . . your big talk. She came to see me, for she was, how do you say, conflicted?'

'Yes?'

'She is not a young woman any longer, Geoffrey: she will be twenty-four next year. She is naturally tempted by any offers that come her way, not least from so distinguished a gentleman as yourself.'

'Yes?'

'Of course. And besides, she likes you. She told me so. You would be very flattered, I am sure, if I recounted all she said.'

'Tell me.'

'She said you were the most interesting Englishman she had ever met.'

'Did she? Did she really?'

'Yes. She did.'

'My word.'

'She said she had rarely met a man whose intellectual curiosity so closely paralleled her own.'

'Did she? Did she really?'

'Yes. She did.'

'My *word*.'

'She said that if marriage came down to companionship, cultural common ground, mutual backgrounds and senses of humour, she would be insane to let your generous offer pass her by.'

'Louise said that?'

'Yes, she did.'

'But, presumably, there was more?'

'Yes. There was more. I hope this won't come as a shock to you, Geoffrey, and I hesitate to speak of this subject behind a woman's back, but—'

'Yes? Yes?'

'—Louise, my dear friend Louise, is not entirely without . . . a *past*.'

'No!'

'Yes.'

'She told you this, as well?'

'Geoffrey,' I sighed. 'Geoffrey. It pains me to say this. I, myself, have had first-hand knowledge of Louise. She claims still to be in love with me.'

Because my hand was on your shoulder I could feel it when your knees buckled. You steadied yourself on the back of an armchair.

'You!' you may have exclaimed, or perhaps it was an involuntary expulsion of air.

'Let me get you a glass of something.'

I returned from the bar to find you slumped at the piano, picking out an original funeral march. I sat on the bench next to you and handed you your drink. Rarely had I seen so blue a man. I contributed a few upper-register harmonies to your dirge, then tried to rationalize your predicament.

'Look at it this way,' I said. 'She may have spared you a certain amount of future embarrassment. I won't pretend she isn't a marvellous girl, and I don't blame you for being disappointed. But you don't strike me as the kind of man who would accept the . . . the *flexible* arrangement that a girl like Louise might demand.'

You choked on your anger. It required an effort for you to look me in the eye. You swallowed the first three or four words you wanted to say. At last you gathered sufficient strength to formulate a sentence of sorts: 'Pierre, you rotter,' you said.

'I beg your pardon?'

'I believe you deliberately introduced me to one of your . . . one of your *women*, in an effort to disgrace me. Again.'

Naturally I argued that this was not the case. Remember? But you were overcome, having fallen in love for the first time – then quickly out of it – in a matter of days. I suggested that you might be grateful for my having provided you with the raw material of such an experience in the delectable form of Louise, but you were not thinking clearly. You stormed out of my house, out of my neighbourhood, out of Paris, out of France. You did not return for three months, a period I spent – and I don't know if I have ever told you this – entirely in the company of Louise.

While rightly omitting any mention of this episode, your Chapter Two wrongly implies that our relationship somehow 'improved' during that winter. In fact, our only communication during your absence was a confusing letter from you, written at Dollsworthy, which expressed your by then solidified belief that I had 'stolen' Louise from you; and my reply, if I recall correctly, which was warm and sympathetic even as it contradicted you. I had Louise add a postscript as confirmation. My God, but Louise and I were having fun.

So you and I were off to a rocky start, with only David Debrizzi to unite us. If I behaved at all badly – though I will not confess to having deliberately arranged Louise's snub – it was a natural reaction to the threat you posed to my close understanding with David. When you returned to Paris I was happy to see that you became embroiled in *Foray Into Fauré*, and kept your distance. It was only when you finished your book that you cast an eye on 'our' pupil and pronounced him ripe for public display.

Your

CHAPTER THREE

What a serene and charming boy David was, and how deceptive were these traits: beneath that waveless surface swam the leviathan – feeding, growing, breeding – of David Debrizzi's talent. To see his Gift, I humbly confess, shaped my very view of God.

This moving passage reminded me of our heated Nature/ Nurture debates over cognac at the Père et Fils. You found it convenient to give credit to a deity for David's admittedly remarkable ability to play the piano. This shows, I think, how much we revere music. If a man plays well, he is 'gifted'; if he plays supremely well – too well, perhaps, like Paganini – he may be suspected of Satanic compromises. I was uneasy during these discussions because modesty prevented me from using the evidence of my own experience: as a teenager I was every bit as good as David, yet I had neither forged links with Mephistopheles, nor felt the hand of God upon my brow. What I remember most of my 'natural gift' is hour after knuckle-aching hour at the piano, morning, afternoon and evening, for *ten years*, before I was considered a 'naturally gifted' fourteen year old. I dare say ten years spent studying medicine at that pace would have qualified me for the status of 'miraculously gifted teenage brain-surgeon'. Playing the piano all day is a bizarre activity for a small child, and probably unfair. We explain away this guilty realization by imputing divine origins to the prodigy's miserable task. My occasional temper tantrum or refusal to play was inevitably chalked up to yet another facet of my 'genius', rather than to normal, childlike boredom and impatience.

There are two rules for making a child into a prodigy: be musical; be cruel. You must be musical, not for hereditary reasons, but in order to increase the likelihood that you will own a piano, and know what to do with it; you must be cruel, because it is cruel to addict your child to a grinding work schedule at the keyboard, then simultaneously to boast about and justify the child's solitary, gruelling life by labelling it a 'gift'. That David Debrizzi's parents were seemingly sweet and harmless people does not convince me that they were not cruel to their son; we are all collaborators on that count.

I was a trained animal. I lived for the approbation of my teachers and parents the way a dolphin will perform flips, smiling, for food. To the limit of my mental and physical strength I toiled at the keyboard. The result – the only visible, provable, positive result – was that I awoke into teenaged consciousness possessing an ability to play the piano very, *very* well indeed. The only mystery was why anyone considered it mysterious.

> *For God had blessed this child threefold, with Talent, with Temperament, with Taste.*

Before allowing your text to descend any further into pious sentimentality, you revert to the more mundane matter of criticizing me:

> *Pierre Marie La Valoise disagreed with my plans for David. I fully understood his worries, as well as his personal insecurities. Because he saw in David*

his pianistic reincarnation, La Valoise understandably
believed that to place the boy on stage was to invite
a revisitation of the dreaded curse of his own past.
David's failure might compound that of La Valoise,
which, for the rather vulnerable Frenchman, would
have proved psychologically intolerable.

It is true that I disagreed with your forceful proposal that
David perform his début at the Salle Thierry the following
spring, aged nine and a half; and who am I to argue with
your psychoanalysis? You are, after all, the same man who
has written at length, for no reasons other than scholarly
integrity and large amounts of money, that George Sand
may have *murdered* Chopin because she envied his genius.
Where no medical nor forensic evidence exists to support
your hypothesis, you conclude quite unassailably that she
had motive, she dressed oddly, she had opportunity and,
after all, *Chopin was dead*. By skillfully recreating a vivid
version – your own – of George Sand's lack of remorse,
you make all but the most hard-hearted readers believe
that poor, tender-souled, unsuspecting Chopin was killed
off by 'a villain history will never forgive'. The mind boggles.
Conspiracy theorists everywhere drool in agreement.

In the same way, you hope to convince your readers that I
had already begun to sabotage David's fledgling career simply
in order to preserve my own fragile sanity. What reader would
be satisfied with the truth, as I see it? When you suggested
David perform, I said, sanely, 'I disagree. Not just yet. There
is no need. He will be better in a few years.' I felt no great need
to justify this point of view, and was not unduly distressed
when I was overruled by you and David's parents. Like the
good junior adviser that I was, I made my point, accepted
defeat, and set about trying to make David's début as much
fun as possible.

Even you admit that David was nervous. You had seen
how uninhibited he was at home, how much he loved to
show off, so perhaps you didn't quite realize how much he
dreaded performing in front of a large number of strangers.

You soon saw, of course. You even witnessed David's first tears of frustration when you corrected him on a point not of music, but of *presentation*.

'You are leaning too far forward,' you dared to say to the child, who was playing beautifully. 'Try it again with your head higher. We want them to see your face, David.'

His tears were instantaneous, and therefore more frightening than the average sob. I took you into the kitchen and pressed my point one last time. I begged you to put off the concert, but by then it was too late: Igor was on the scene.

Igor. Igor Malechievich. You must recoil at the name. No doubt you refrained from a lengthy assault on the young Igor in your *Life*, because the man is still alive and thriving.

> *Another factor had entered the equation of my decision-making process vis-à-vis David's first performance. Igor Malechievich – today a most respected and successful solo pianist whose latest recordings are awaited with bated breath by his legion fans – had announced his intention to take Paris by storm in the early summer. Igor was eleven years old. I thought it more advisable than ever to present David's skills to the public before they could be unfairly pre-empted by the child from Leningrad.*

Yes, absolutely. This is the music-as-chess-game school of prodigy management. While I disagreed with this premise, I could not help sharing your fear of the diabolical Igor. I had dreaded him for years, for David's sake.

Among Igor's annoying mannerisms, you will recall, was the symbolic throwing-down of the gauntlet before each performance (he had been doing this since the age of four). He skipped on to the stage – I will be the first to admit that he looked a bit like me, robust and severe for his years – wiped his brow with a white handkerchief, then flung it on to the floor at the foot of the stage. The handkerchief remained there, like a flower, illuminated by its own spotlight, for the duration of his performance.

Who do you think taught him that trick? His father, of course.

Igor travelled with an entourage. Igor wore a white silk fighter-pilot's scarf. Igor threw regular tantrums. Igor ate nothing but wild mushrooms and drank no liquid but cranberry juice. Some people even believed that Igor, since his tenth birthday, had become an accomplished lover. He crammed every trait of adult prima donnas into his childhood, presaging his sometimes chilling behaviour of today. Like so many 'prodigies' – here David was a notable exception – Igor lived under the influence of at least one monstrous parent. In Igor's case this role was amply filled by his terrifying father, a Leningrad war-hero and impresario, a man so awesome he could have reduced Rasputin to tears with a well-chosen word and a stare. Even though he died four years ago, Igor's father gets off lightly in your book; I wouldn't blame you if you had feared he would return from the dead to wreak his revenge. You write only that without the 'energetic coaching' and 'forceful prodding' of Boris Malechievich, young Igor might not have achieved so much, so soon.

In Paris that spring, we trembled in anticipation of the Russian invasion. The only decision to be made, after I had cravenly acceded to your plan to put David on the stage, was whether 'our' performance would precede or follow Igor's.

We knew what Igor would play. Igor always played the same thing. Igor would throw down his gauntlet, plop himself down with a grunt, glare at the keyboard, and perform a rip-roaring Rachmaninov – medium tempo, high volume, startling dynamics – the sort of performance that makes all but the freak-watchers begin to hate music; the kind of performance, in other words, that *I* used to give.

You and I agreed – I like to think it was my idea – that David would play something shorter and prettier, that he would play a diverse set of pieces, that what he played would be suitable to the temperament of a child slowly discovering the wonder of music. With this shared purpose in mind, you and I were able to set aside our previous discord.

53

Against my better instincts, I set about training David for the fateful day. I did not tell him about Igor, there being no way he could hear about the marauding Russians on his own. We settled on a nifty programme of Chopin, Debussy, Schumann and Rachmaninov, all short pieces containing just enough bravura passages that even hardened Igor-worshippers would be inclined to give the younger David his due.

Two weeks before David's concert, Igor crashed into Paris. Posters appeared everywhere. The Salle Thierry sold out. You and I hid our apprehension from David, and bought back-row seats. The newspapers carried stories and photos of Igor in his hotel suite, at his favourite restaurant (cranberry juice in hand), strolling the boulevards, holding hands with his toothsome twenty-year-old companion, Tanya, in the Tuileries. Igor spoke like a seasoned maestro. His every remark carried inexplicable weight. His faith in numerology captured the imagination of his more mystical fans. 'I am eleven years old,' he said, in French, to an awestruck interviewer. 'One, one. Eleven. *Eleven*. Give that some thought.'

Boris went to great lengths to circulate the myth – which follows Igor to this day – that his son 'never practised'. You, Geoffrey, may even have been taken in by this senseless charade – as if 'not practising' somehow made Igor's music more satisfying. 'He never practises!' people said to each other. 'Can you imagine that? His talent is a gift from God!'

It was a cool May evening in 1966. We met at the Père et Fils for a snack and a drink before our journey across the river to the Salle Thierry. We pretended not to be worried, and said that even if we were perhaps *slightly* interested in viewing the 'competition', well, music wasn't like that: David's music would speak for itself, for better or worse. Piano playing wasn't boxing, after all, we argued. And who really paid attention to child prodigies? David wouldn't come into his own for – what, ten, fifteen, even twenty years? What was a circus-like début at age nine next to a lifetime - a professional career? And if David failed miserably, if he wanted to give up, he seemed to have a head for numbers

– he could become an accountant! By the time we arrived at the packed Salle Thierry, we had worked ourselves into such a frenzy of nerves that we agreed it was *beneath* David to become a pianist, that we would do everything we could to talk him out of it.

Half of the audience at the Salle Thierry was comprised of adoring fans imported from all over Europe by the enterprising and well-connected Boris Malechievich. The remainder included thrill-seekers, idol-worshippers, frustrated teenaged musicians, sceptics, journalists, friends Igor had made since arriving in Paris – and a dozen girls who hoped only to touch the sleeve of the famous prodigy.

Your version of the event, clipped and dismissive, gives no clue to our agitated state of mind. It is easy to say, in hindsight, that we were not the slightest bit concerned – that, in fact, we didn't care if David had to cancel his own début in the wake of Igor's hideous triumph. But I assure you we sat in the back row like students awaiting examination results. We knew that we faced the first test of our faith in David Debrizzi, and that part of one small, adorable child's future hung in the balance.

Over-enthusiastic applause greeted Igor's sudden, dramatic entrance. Tall for his age and overweight – I have already conceded that he looked something like me – Igor quick-stepped to the piano, wiped his brow, flung down his white handkerchief, and seated himself at the closed keyboard. He had affected a brand-new artifice: with an abrupt motion he threw open the piano lid, waited only long enough for the *bang* to subside in the hall, then forged directly *not* into Rachmaninov, as we had predicted, but, God help him, into the *Appassionata*. We exchanged a grim look, set our teeth, and began willing poor Igor to come unglued.

The *Appassionata* is a piece I detest, especially the first movement, which has always sounded to me like the random, improvised accompaniment to a particularly melodramatic silent film, with nauseating glimpses of 'The Star Spangled Banner' thrown in. The *Andante con moto* that follows must have caught Beethoven in a juvenile mood – as if he had just discovered the tensions inherent in the suspended chord – and is devoid of meaning for me; when I was a little boy I used to play it upside down for amusement. Only the third movement – the one a friend of Beethoven's claimed the composer had improvised in its entirety after a particularly long and refreshing walk – presents a technical challenge, but retains the sublime ugliness of that period of Beethoven's *oeuvre*.

I do not know if you shared my misgivings about the *Appassionata*, but as we sat in the Salle Thierry wishing all ills to descend upon Igor, our thoughts were not on the merits of the piece. I clenched my hands on the arm rests. You squinted into the gloom. We were a two-brained force-field of evil in an auditorium overflowing with goodwill.

Igor was then, and is now, a quirky player – so much so that I had to ask myself repeatedly if what I had just heard was an inexcusable gaffe, or an original brilliancy. The first movement fled by without my being able to form an opinion of his playing.

Igor was not one simply to bang out the notes, we had to hand him that. Much height had been added to his bench, so that he was able to contort himself over the piano with his cheek parallel to the keys. In the second movement he elicited a murmur from the audience when he suddenly opened his eyes and *stared* at the front row, looking from face to face in a searching manner, as if trying to remember their names.

It is odd to think of two grown men heaping psychic warfare upon a child of eleven who is only trying to play Beethoven as well as he can in front of a large audience. But I think you will agree that by the time Igor rounded the corner into the third movement we were both concentrating as hard as we could just on the off chance that paranormal powers existed and we could blow the little bastard off the stage. He had played quite beautifully up to that point. I am sure that in those days I would have sworn on Chopin's grave in Père Lachaise that music transcended base competitive instincts, that money and renown played no part in the discipline. But there I sat, a hypocrite, begging the gods to let a drop of sweat fall beneath Igor's fingers and derail him.

Igor played on. He showed himself to be every bit a Russian: his technique left nothing to be desired. His tone was stoical, his interpretation was wintry. Igor's sound was monolithic, like Lenin's tomb.

And then he made a mistake. Igor blundered in a way that made me hate myself for wishing disaster to befall him, for a disaster this certainly was. For a moment I thought he had suffered the same cruel hallucinations as I, on the same stage: a descending run unravelled beneath his right hand; trying to recover, he failed; trying to repeat the run – his performance already marred beyond repair – he seemed to forget his place in the music. He retreated several bars in order to gain forward momentum, and failed to negotiate the run once again. The audience groaned.

Then Igor did something that earned him a permanent measure of my respect. He put his hands in his lap. He bowed his head for a full fifteen seconds. He turned to the audience and said, in French, in his prepubescent voice, 'Pardon me. I will start again.'

Start again he did, and this built such tension as he neared the previously fatal run that I doubt any audience in a century and a half had ever listened to the third movement of the *Appassionata* in a state of such unbearable excitement. You could hear the people shifting to the edges of their seats. I was, by this time, entirely on Igor's side. Inwardly I cheered him on, just as I scolded myself for my previous cold-heartedness.

The run neared. The audience tensed as one muscle. Igor – and all the journalists noticed – actually *smiled*. The dreaded run sprayed into the hall like seeds blown from a dandelion, and the audience burst into spontaneous 'Aaahs' and virtually involuntary clapping. Igor sped to the end of the piece and landed on those last three chords with such triumphant force that the piano moved six inches across the stage.

We joined in the standing ovation.

'My *word*!' you shouted over the roar. 'Do you think old *Boris* taught him to do that?'

I am surprised – suspicious, even – that your version of this event reads, in its entirety, as follows:

> *A short while before David's début, La Valoise and I took the opportunity to witness eleven-year-old Igor Malechievich's Paris début. He played the* Appassionata - *competently, we agreed; he did not pose a threat to David's ambitions.*

Did not pose a threat? We left the Salle Thierry amid the ecstatic hordes, and slunk off to the nearest café for a necessary drink, moaning like war widows and wishing we'd never got involved with the Debrizzis.

Standing at the copper bar, not looking at each other, we decided to address the crisis logically. There were two explanations for what we had witnessed: that Igor had genuinely stumbled, then recovered in so gracious and courageous a fashion that he deserved a footnote in the history of piano recitals as one of the most self-possessed prodigies of all time; or that Boris had arranged this stunt with his malleable son in order to win the favour of a Western capital – in which case Igor's would be an unstoppably calculating public relations machine with which no fellow performer, least of all the soft-spoken David, could hope to compete.

Not only did we think young Igor posed a threat but, I am ashamed to admit, we were on the verge of pulling David out of his own performance 'for reasons of health'. You managed to convince me that to cancel David's concert so soon after Igor's would fool no one, and that we might attract less attention to our strategic disaster if we went ahead with the show. We agreed to quash all publicity and hope that no one showed up at the Salle Thierry to watch him. In front of the Debrizzis we feigned nonchalance. In private we tried to rekindle our optimism by rationalizing Igor's valiant showing as a one-off success, and by stressing the objectionable aspects of his overwrought persona.

You leave out of your biography any mention of my meeting with Boris Malechievich, which I kept secret from you for five years because I was so embarrassed. I don't believe I ever told you the full story.

Boris rang me at home, one week after Igor's concert, one week before David's. How he got my number I do not know. We arranged to meet at the Oiselet, because I thought a Russian even of Boris's standing might find it difficult to get his fill of good *foie gras*. I tried phoning you to inform you of this unusual communication between opposing camps, but your concierge told me you had gone to Amsterdam for the weekend.

I couldn't imagine what Boris wanted, and feared that he might try to hypnotize me with that stare of his in order to undermine my teaching powers. I wore sunglasses and a crucifix against this possibility. I waited in the restaurant for half an hour before Boris made his entrance, alone. I was glad he hadn't brought Igor along, who would have required an extra table for his entourage; they didn't serve cranberry juice at the Oiselet. Boris wore a gigantic double-breasted Savile Row-imitation three-piece wide-striped winter-wool suit, though it was a hot and smoky day. The restaurant darkened significantly as he loomed in the doorway looking for my comparatively small self.

Because Boris shared many of his son's eccentricities, my friends at the Oiselet spent a quarter of an hour scurrying about changing lights, removing plants, asking a woman please to take her dog outside, scouring a brown spot of insect remains on the wall near Boris's seat, and assuring their Russian patron over and over again that their kitchen had not been lacking in garlic cloves for the lifetime of the restaurant. When all of that business had been taken care of to Boris's grudging satisfaction, the big man sat down and froze me with his humourless blue eyes. I removed my sunglasses, as if hypnotized into doing so.

'Do you speak French?' I asked him, in my rusty Russian.

'*Nyet*,' said Boris, so Russian it was.

'Your son was marvellous. How proud you must be.'

'*Da*,' said Boris. He had not yet blinked.

'I must say I was surprised to hear from you. You had heard of me?'

'*Da*,' said Boris, nodding his great head. When he stopped moving his skull it took his flesh an extra two nods to settle. 'I was in the audience – what, eight or nine years ago? I saw you.'

'Oh, my, you mean . . . you mean you saw me *explode*?'

'*Da*. I am sorry.'

'I am a fatalist, Mr Malechievich. It was not meant to be. And I am not an unhappy man.' This was my usual speech. In fact, it was untrue. I seethed with anger over my failure, and I was anything but a fatalist in those days. And as for happiness, well, *I ask you*.

'I am glad to hear that you are happy. But now I must tell you why I wished to see you. It is a delicate thing I must ask, but since you have said you are not regretful, perhaps I may continue?'

'As you wish.' Our *foie gras* and wine had arrived, but because Boris continued to stare me straight in the eye I was unable to begin eating.

'You were there last week. You saw Igor. You saw how magnificent he was.' Igor had not reached his precocious international standing due to parental humility.

'Yes.'

'But you also saw his . . . little difficulty.'

'Yes, of course, but—'

'It is impermissible. It will stop.'

I fingered the crucifix against my chest between the buttons of my shirt. Boris had leaned halfway over the table, his tie perilously close to his goose liver, and seemed to be blaming *me* for his son's entirely understandable lapse on stage.

'I tell this to Igor. I say to him that he will not fail again or – forgive me – what happened to you will happen to him. Oh, yes, I have told him the story many times. I told him how

60

marvellous you were, how your Rachmaninov was the envy of every Russian, how we feared you. And I told him how, well, as you put it, how you *exploded*. Igor was impressed by this story and it has made him concentrate. He very much wanted to meet you. I told him I did not think that was advisable.'

Boris apparently believed that I was a viral carrier of failure.

'I hope my example can be of some help to him,' I said, straining to remain polite.

If Boris had been merely hinting up to that point that my presence in the Salle Thierry might somehow have transmitted my virus to Igor, he left no doubt any longer.

'I was not pleased to find out you were in the hall,' he said. 'I *felt* you. Then my people told me you were in fact there. Only out of sympathy did I allow you to remain. I do not wish to make the same mistake again.' Even in a good mood, Boris Malechievich intimidated all who came into contact with him; an angry Boris Malechievich was positively searing. I am sure that I recoiled from this last remark, and wished I could start my meal. Above all I did not want to lose my temper. I had no desire to know if Boris's reputation for physical violence rested on fact.

'I do not know why you came to the concert,' said Boris. Without interrupting his trademark glare, he sliced a huge piece of liver and scooped it between his bulbous lips. That one mouthful probably contained more calories than he had eaten in an average month during the siege of Leningrad. He chewed grotesquely. 'I do not know why you came, unless it was to fulfill a ghoulish fantasy of seeing to it that all talented youngsters who followed in your trail were destroyed.'

This line of argument I could have tolerated, especially as I wished to leave the restaurant with my features intact. Having established that Boris was indeed a madman, I needed only to ride out our discussion without further antagonizing him. But he found a different tack, which made it impossible for me to restrain myself.

'Because I know this to be true of you,' said Boris, 'I can safely assume that you will be present next week at the concert of the French boy, David Debrizzi.' So he didn't know of my work with David. 'I expect that you will be there, just as you were there when Igor played, in order to cast your wicked spell.'

'Mr Malechievich,' I began, wishing to put him straight at the outset, 'I really should tell you that—'

'Hush!' boomed Boris. 'I will not hear your excuses. It would be quite easy for me to do the dishonourable thing and allow you to subvert the performance of a rival. But I have too much respect for the work of *all* musical children to allow your witchcraft to interfere again. Besides, I very much admire the Debrizzi child's teacher, Mr Geoffrey Flynch, about whom you have no doubt heard a great deal. I will not stand still and see his hard work go out the window.' Naturally this last comment enraged me, but I could not get a word through the denseness of Boris's voice; in any case my Russian had begun to fail me. 'Most importantly,' he said, more softly but with still greater intensity, 'I want my son to be there, to see David play. And I will not have him in the same room with *you*.' Boris flung one of his fleshy fingers across the table at me.

I had now absorbed a series of not-so-subtle insults; I had to make myself heard. I wrenched my feeble Russian back to life, and spoke in a near shout.

'David is *my* pupil,' I said. 'Igor can piss off to Vladivostok, for all I care. You are a paranoid megalomaniac.' I surprised myself not only with the violence of my words, but with remembering them in Russian.

Boris's face reddened at my crude, *ad hominem* attack. His already bulging eyes showed twice again as much white.

'You will *not* speak about my son that way!' he bellowed. My faithful friends of the Oiselet cautiously drew nearer. 'You will *not* speak about my *son* that way!' He waved his hands as if reaching the climax of a patriotic address.

'Your *son*,' I said, with the rash sarcasm of a man who has been stung, and who possesses a limited vocabulary in a foreign language, 'isn't fit to turn David's pages.'

Now Boris's eyes, unable to bulge wider, squinted fiend-
ishly. He seemed to hope for a moment that he had misunder-
stood my French-accented Russian. When he realized that his
ears had not deceived him – and when he saw my snide smirk
– Boris erupted.

A noise began deep within his barrel chest as he raised
himself a few inches from the banquette. I cringed into my
chair, hoping Boris would rein in his temper. I had been
physically assaulted only once before, by my older brother,
and knew that I hated being hit. I bruised easily about the
face, and my hands, though powerful, were not to be risked
even in extreme self-defence.

Boris moved around the table with his hands outstretched,
like a strangler. The noise, which had begun as a crepitation,
had reached such volume that the employees of the Oiselet
retreated hastily in the direction of the kitchen. I spluttered
a few diplomatic words to Boris before he grasped me by
the neck, trying to convey to him the more rational side of
our misunderstanding. In fact I am certain that in my terror
I offered to withdraw David not only from the imminent
recital, but from the concert circuit in general, and to publish
my own view that Igor Malechievich reigned supreme in
the prodigy world. In the throes of rage, Boris was deaf
to my pleas.

As you – and now your readers – know very well, I have
always been a heavy-set man. It was all the more surprising,
therefore, to feel myself being lifted high off the ground by
the neck. I laughed, in a panicky and strangulated way. Boris
put me down to free a hand with which to hit me. He cuffed
me across the jaw. I felt as if I had been struck by the
rear-view mirror of a London bus – I think of this because it
happened to me only five years ago – and I tasted blood. The
craven waiters of the Oiselet allowed me to be pummelled by
the Russian, looking on like bored spectators of gladitorial
combat. To this day I am served free wine by the owner as a
small recompense for his staff's cowardice. I was revived by
a warm dishtowel, and found that Boris had left the premises.
He had taken our bottle of wine with him. I called my doctor

from the restaurant and asked him to meet me at my house for emergency treatment, that is to say brandy and cigarettes.

I kept this story from you not only because I thought it was embarrassing to be battered by a gigantic Russian lunatic, but because I was ashamed to have learned that Boris knew of your involvement with David, and not mine. I told you some version of the story five years later only in the context of accusation: I suspected that you had contacted Boris and told him of your activities without mentioning mine. I considered this a betrayal. This would explain why your Chapter Three skips over the incident – and why the entire period I have just covered requires only a single page-turn from your credulous readership. One moment you have descended on Paris to 'take charge' of David, and the next the child bows before the plaudits of a packed Salle Thierry. Biography is a demanding craft; let me supply a few more details.

David never learned anything about Boris and Igor in Paris. I explained my bruised face by telling the most elaborate lie: David liked stories. I told him my maid had called in sick, that in advance of a glamorous dinner party I had attempted a bit of tidying on my own, that the feather duster I employed for the purpose had knocked a priceless vase from the mantelpiece, that I had dived like a volleyball player to catch the object before it smashed on my marble floor, that I had juggled the vase before drawing it into my arms, that I had sacrificed my face to the floor rather than break a work of art. I drew a moral out of the story pertaining to the value of truth and beauty, compared to transient human life. David liked, and believed, my story.

Three days before David's recital I went walking with him in the Parc Monçeau. We talked about his friends and classmates and intolerant teachers, and I tried to avoid any mention of his imminent début – the thought of which sent electrical surges down my arms into my retired fingertips. It was David who raised the subject.

'Mr Flynch says there will be two hundred people there,' said David. He had never asked about the audience before, only the music.

'That is the capacity of the hall,' I replied. 'This is show-business. We must never get our hopes up or even contemplate such things. Leave the worrying to Mr Flynch. If no one buys a ticket, you can perform for me and for your parents. You'll have fun. Actually, and I shouldn't be telling you this, a lot of tickets have been sold in advance.'

'Why do they want to watch me play?'

A tricky question. I motioned towards a bench so that I could equivocate while sitting down.

'You already know why,' I said, making the mistake of treating David like an ordinary child. 'It is because they like listening to music, and you play the music so well.'

'*You* could play,' said David. 'You could play even louder than I can.'

David liked his piano music loud.

'It has something to do with your being slightly younger than I am,' I said. 'You have to admit that you are still fairly young.'

'I'm nine years old.'

'Exactly right. People think it is amazing that a nine-year-old boy can do something they wish they could do, and that they know they couldn't do in a million years.'

'A million years,' said David, who liked numbers. 'A thousand thousand. Not so huge as it sounds. Anyway, they probably could if they really wanted to.'

'Perhaps. The fact remains that they will enjoy seeing you do it. You will have so much fun when you hear them applauding.'

Sitting on the bench, David's feet didn't reach the ground. Pigeons walked beneath his sandals. He frowned for a moment in thought, then brushed his hair back from his brow and made a statement.

'It will be incumbent upon me,' he said, grandly, 'to give a good account of myself.'

As always we were speaking in English, and there was no mistaking the source of this sentence.

'Did Mr Flynch tell you that?'

'Yes.'

I have always associated the chilling phrase 'to give a good account of oneself' with English memoirists describing their primary concern when presented with the opportunity of striding headlong into machine-gun fire. Such is the sense of doom you had instilled in David, subconsciously, preceding something as comparatively trivial as a piano recital.

'What Mr Flynch means,' I said, patronizing again, 'is that a piano recital is supposed to be fun, and the more you enjoy yourself, the more the audience will enjoy your performance. It is a marvellous thing for a boy your age to be doing. You'll see how marvellous it is.'

' " Marvellous," ' David mimicked. 'It makes me perspire.'

'Come on,' I said. 'We'll get you a lemonade on the way home. I have an idea. We're going to play a little joke on Mr Flynch.'

'Oh, *good*,' said David. David liked games.

Having laid our conspiratorial plans, David and I silently suffered two days of your pep-talking, back-slapping, stiff-upper-lipping, over-the-top-boys, good-account-of-oneself sermonizing. Had David and I not shared a secret and reassuring scheme, I would have begged you to desist.

On the day of the concert I was so numbed by nervousness that I felt like a decerebrated zombie. Even Gabrielle and Anita were at pains to put me right. I began dressing for the evening concert at noon, applying cold compresses to my chapped and feverish face. I met you at the Debrizzi's house where we collected David and his somewhat agitated parents. Greta, David's grandmother, who more than anyone was responsible for the child's having learned to play at such an early age, declared her unwillingness to be a party to 'exhibitionism'. She kissed David goodbye at the door and enjoined him to 'play as loudly as possible', and 'not to think about the germs'. David looked confused by this, so we bundled him out the door into my car before he could ask Greta what she meant.

You remarked, unhelpfully, that owing to the wet and chilly conditions David ought to keep his hands wrapped in a scarf. It really did seem to me that you were doing everything in your power to cause the child distress. I told David not to worry, that we would soak his hands in hot water before his performance. I tried to make this sound like fun.

We entered the checkered-floor foyer of the Salle Thierry exactly one hour before David was scheduled to play. To our great surprise there were people queuing at the ticket booth, waiting to snap up the seats of no-shows. Our quiet publicity had backfired. The press had fed greedily on the Igor/David duel, and had called upon the Parisian public to show their support for the local boy. Our relative restraint, compared with Boris's publicity juggernaut, had only served to fuel the newspapers' zeal in ensuring a high profile when David's turn came.

People began to notice David as we ushered him through the lobby. 'Look!' one cried. 'He is so small!' David stopped and raised an eyebrow at the man. I could see that he wanted to say 'I'm only *nine*, after all,' but I managed to herd him towards the staircase and safety.

In the dressing room David's parents sat on wooden classroom chairs with their hands folded on their knees, sharing an expression of fear and regret at having agreed to put their boy through such a stressful experience. You paced nerve-rackingly back and forth while lecturing David in an unmodulated voice about the importance of concentration and relaxation.

'Relax!' you shouted at him, bits of saliva and phlegm flying across the room. '*Relax!*'

David inspected make-up cases, looked in every drawer, found amusing bits of theatrical costume. I believe I shared with you a paranoid sense that we had hallucinated David's talent all along – that we had duped his parents into believing in him also – and that we were four adults trapped in a dressing room with an oblivious little boy whose only interest for the moment was in feather boas and pots of eyeliner.

'David!' you shouted at him. '*Please* relax!'

David turned off the tap he had been toying with and gave us all an alarmed look.

'What's wrong?' he asked. 'Why is everyone shouting?'

'Here,' I said, my voice raised easily a fifth from the norm, 'let's fill the basin and soak your hands!'

The next fifteen minutes passed in silence as David stood at the sink with his sleeves rolled up and his hands plunged in hot water. The manager of the Salle Thierry came by to see that all was in order, and shook David's hot, wet hand. He seemed not to like prodigies, or their families, and left after perfunctory wishes of good luck and '*bon courage*'.

'Now if you don't mind,' I said, with half an hour to go, 'David and I would like to warm up alone.'

You were not pleased with this arrangement, but read in David's face his desire that you and his parents ought to depart. (This is at variance with your version of the pre-concert preparations, in which I do not figure at all.)

'I will see you backstage,' you said, and after more hysterical advice to David you stumbled away with Henri and Camille right behind you.

David sat at the upright piano and placed his little pink hands on the keys. I admit it: I thought I would have a heart attack. I stood behind him, out of sight, rubbing my face and drying the sweat on my trousers. This was the same piano I had warmed up on before my own humiliating concert at the Salle Thierry, with Monsieur Presteron pacing angrily behind me, counting slips and muttering vague obscenities under his breath. Although David was much younger than I had been, I thought I knew what he felt. His cool, even distracted exterior must have concealed an interior anxiety that went well beyond nerves, into a black, pulsing region of the unconscious. Stage fright, I assure you, is of metaphysical origin. Hence the expression, oft heard behind the curtains of the world's stages, 'What am I doing here?'

'I'll leave you alone for a minute,' I said, more for my own benefit than his. 'I'm going to take a look at the hall.' David nodded without interrupting his scales.

Weak-kneed, I crept down the hallway to the stairs. I leaned over the banister and saw the milling crowd in the lobby. I asked myself who they were, or, as David

68

had wondered in the Parc Monçeau, why they wished to watch a young boy play hackneyed piano music. They were young, informally dressed, many unaccompanied. I decided they were all, or nearly all, failed musicians or parents of promising children. Like soccer fans, they wanted to relive the hopes of their youth, or to confirm in their minds the potential of their offspring.

I could delve no deeper into the matter as my harried thoughts were interrupted by the self-important entrance of the Igor Malechievich entourage. Boris cleared a path through the lobby with his great head held high and his beefy hands breast-stroking a swathe through the crowd. Little Igor, bescarved and dramatically insouciant, followed behind on the arm of the mouthwatering Tanya. With Boris waving a clutch of tickets in the air, they made their way without pausing into the hall. I rushed to the back stairs, pushed past you and the Debrizzis, and peeked from behind the curtain. Down the aisle they came, straight to the front row. Boris ushered his son and his private army into their seats, then sat down, on the aisle. The group sat immobile, their voodoo stares fixed on the empty, spotlit piano. You came up behind me, beheld the scene, and hissed anti-Soviet epithets.

'Never mind,' I said. 'David will never notice.'

I bounded back upstairs and found David deep in conversation with the formerly hostile stage manager.

'Look!' said David, when he saw me. 'We can play a duet!'

He and the manager sat side by side at the upright and banged out a gruesome 'Chopsticks' variation while I seethed near the door. Just managing to keep my temper, I applauded them, then politely asked the man to leave David alone.

'Five minutes,' he said. He beamed at the irresistible David, then slammed the door behind him.

'Are you all set?' I asked the boy. I had begun to regret our pre-arranged practical joke.

'Yes. Mr Flynch will be so surprised. You must tell me how he reacts afterwards.'

'Of course I will. Now play me a bit of the Debussy, and then we'll go downstairs.'

Five minutes later I stood backstage with one hand on David's shoulder, listening to the clearing of throats as the lights dimmed in the hall. David's parents had taken their seats at the front of the balcony. You were there at my side leaning against the concrete wall near the curtain ropes, green and unsteady.

'Out you go, then,' I said, kissing David on the temple and patting his bottom.

'Pierre,' he said (for he called me Pierre).

'Yes?'

'Watch me wink.'

I had been teaching David to wink. He opened his blue eyes wide, then scrunched one of them shut using his nose, eyebrow and cheek. I winked back. He turned and walked out on to the stage.

I had expected the audience to gasp, and gasp they did. Unlike Igor Malechievich, whose swaggering entrance commanded respectful silence, David shuffled on to the boards in his navy-blue jacket and shorts, and looked so small and out of place, so dwarfed by the concert grand, that even these virtuoso-vultures were audibly startled. Their reaction stopped David in his tracks. He looked up into the lights from beneath his dark fringe and took in his first sight of an audience, his first sensation of being at the centre of things.

'Go on, David,' you and I whispered in unison, not loud enough for him to hear. 'Go *on*.'

David seemed frozen on the spot. For several seconds I thought the concert would be over before it had begun, that David's stage-fright would exceed even mine in its intensity, until I realized the boy was searching the audience for his parents. When he found that he could not pick out Henri and Camille beyond the lights, he issued a tiny wave anyway, and a smile so adorably winning that even a few of Igor's entourage found themselves smiling back.

The ice was broken. The audience settled. David walked to the gigantic piano and sat down with his back to us. Unlike the older Igor, David did not require the crutch of music on the stand. David and the piano, alone together with a painful silence and composers' impatient ghosts.

'My word,' you whispered, your knuckles white on a curtain rope. 'Just look at Boris, will you?'

Boris's eyes bulged and glared like glinting lenses of binoculars.

'Never mind,' I said, crossing my fingers behind my back. 'Here he goes.'

Everyone who had glanced at the programme expected to hear the opening legato phrases of Debussy's *Dance Bohémienne*. Especially you, Geoffrey. You had been very much in favour of this piece as a fitting first for a French pianist. You must have tried to prick yourself awake from a nightmare when you heard the first notes that rang from beneath David's fingers. Not only was this not Debussy, you must have thought, but although it sounded vaguely familiar you could not tell at first if the piece had been composed by a reputable musician at all.

It sounded as if David had placed his hands randomly on the keyboard and begun to play, for example, a Chopin Etude in the wrong key – which is what he *was* doing, actually, and more. True *aficionados* would have figured out within seconds that David was playing the Etude Op. 25 No. 1 in two different keys at the same time, neither one faithful to the original. He had started up a fifth in the right hand and down a fifth in the left. It sounded ugly and preposterous, of course, but somehow *right*, in that it followed rules and continued inexorably in the same vein. Then came the beautiful part. Every eight measures David lowered the right-hand by a full tone, and raised the left by the same interval. It was an unnerving, even sacrilegious sound, but the excitement lay in knowing that soon David would arrive in the proper key and Chopin's poetic original would be restored to us – not before some fairly hair-raising dissonances, of course, but that was the whole point.

You should have seen yourself, Geoffrey: slackened jaw, eyebrows arched right off your forehead, left hand suspended pleadingly in the air as if reaching out to turn back a cosmic clock. If you had looked at me you might have been reassured by my knowing smile, but you endured the entire piece believing that David had forgotten how to play, been possessed by the Devil, or fallen prey to Boris's evil eyes.

In hindsight, our little joke looks like one of the great artistic coups of the Parisian musical scene, when of course my real motive had been to give David something to think about other than your schoolmasterly lectures – and of course to give us both the pleasure of seeing you reel in temporary shock. But this *was* Paris, and it *was* 1966, and David's first number caused a healthy storm of debate. The rest of his recital, which came off perfectly, need not have happened. Paris had another *cause célèbre* on its hands. Art had been executed in the Salle Thierry. Artistic practical-joking from a nine year old was newsworthy. The musical ramifications of what David Debrizzi had done were imponderable, some said. And all because of our little game.

Your version, need I add, is slightly different:

> *Despite an irresponsible bit of nonsense orchestrated by La Valoise – who took advantage of David's playful streak in the most cynical and dangerous way – the concert was a smashing success. The Debussy was a dream; the stately Schumann was executed with rare integrity; the Rachmaninov – a deliberate snub to Igor, methinks? – growled through the hall in a way not heard since La Valoise himself had (briefly) set the town alight.*

How kind of you, Geoffrey.

> *I felt a quite paternal relief. My mission to Paris had not been in vain. David Debrizzi was well and truly on his way. Paris was at his feet. A nine-year-old boy had passed his initiation in style, and all that remained was to see to what heights the miraculous little French boy could be guided. I may never have known such pride.*

*

The sun sets again on the Grand Glacier. My doctor now agrees that my writing to you is medically sound. He can see how I look forward to tomorrow, when I can address your Chapter Four, a bit of history notable mostly for what it leaves out: two years during which David did little more than practise the piano; but a time when you discovered love.

Your

CHAPTER FOUR

David toiled at the keyboard, absorbing the music of long-dead masters, while you burst on to the recording scene in London with your psychedelically inspired album, 'Lemon Schubert'. What an ugly time the Sixties were. You selflessly mention this collector's item only to compound the embarrassment by telling us that your preferred title, 'Take Me To Your Lieder', had been overruled by the producer. Only your infrequent base–touching visits to Paris kept you nominally in charge of David's progress, while it was I who coached the boy three days a week.

No, my life did not 'revolve around' David. I was an energetic twenty-five-year-old with a variable private income and a diverse circle of friends. I wrote musical criticism in three languages and played chess with influential philosophers. I applied myself with some diligence to my family's charitable concerns; my older and more responsible brother had monopolized the family's conventional businesses during my father's reluctant retirement.

Anita left my household to marry a young historian friend of mine, and was replaced by a wayward girl, Chantal – a distant enough relation that few eyebrows were raised. You will remember meeting Chantal, and I know you loved her. She

74

was a singer, as her name would suggest, and quite unpredictable at parties. She had a craggy, working–man's face and stringy hair and she smelled like a burnt-down house from cigarettes and only the occasional bath. Her conversation was so cuttingly delightful that most sensible men found her irresistible. She was twenty-two and looked forty. Gabrielle enjoyed the contrast of her company as much as I did.

Honestly, Geoffrey, I am surprised that your publisher's libel lawyers did not consider comparisons between me and the Marquis de Sade somewhat tenuous and risky. The dear old Marquis, who surely suffered enough in his lifetime to have been spared history's scorn, is renowned for behaviour that would not have entered my mind, much less my bedroom. What you fail to see is that my domestic arrangements were always entirely above-board, constantly discussed, and, unlike some of Sade's, *voluntary*. If anything I was egged on by the girls in my life, and I like to think I learned something new from them every day. In many ways I was a conventional sort. You did not realize this, for you express in print your great surprise at my decision to marry Gabrielle in the spring of 1968:

> *This was not the La Valoise I knew, but it gave me some hope that he had begun to mend his ways. I knew Gabrielle, and although she was young and vulnerable to the crude charms of La Valoise, I thought that hers might be a stabilizing influence. Anyone who played a role in David's life was of concern to me, and I did not want to see one of them, especially La Valoise, living a life that could adversely affect David's natural trajectory.*

I would so like your readers to know that you probably lost your virginity in the arms of my first wife. A description of her kisses, even in your convoluted prose, would have been a welcome diversion for a man who, at the time of first reading your book, had not been kissed in several weeks owing to feeding tubes and an oxygen mask.

On a happier note, it was at my wedding that you met *your*

75

first wife. Sarah would probably have been disappointed at being referred to only as 'a future friend', but I suppose you could hardly leave out a reference to someone who had doused a Rolls Royce in cognac and set it alight.

'Sarah' is too bland a name for a woman of your first wife's sensational volatility. I first met Sarah, as she no doubt told you, through Louise, and it was in Louise's company that you first found her at my wedding. I wouldn't be surprised if Sarah's disappointment at being ignored by you in favour of her better-looking girlfriend was what caused her to set the car on fire. She thought it was *your* car. Having thus got your attention – and the attention of my Uncle Regis, whose car it actually was – Sarah set single-mindedly about the task of appropriating your devotion. Sarah had decided to get married, and what Sarah wanted Sarah got. If I know Sarah (and I assure you I do), the next six months were a confusing swirl of rows and reconciliations, passion and passing out, culminating before you knew it in a quiet wedding in Bath. Your son was born and taken home to Dollsworthy before Gabrielle and I had recovered from our honeymoon.

(How *is* Emanuel? Last I heard, the poor boy was having to explain to the authorities at Christ's Church the presence of a bloody syringe in his rooms. Next to wealth, I suppose early divorce is the most likely cause of delinquency. I was very sorry to hear of Sarah's death two years ago, and that she chose to end her life in so public a manner.)

All of this is merely the unmentioned background to your joyful Chapter Four, in which you set out to explain to your readers why it is that David Debrizzi showed early signs of being an important 'artist', rather than a drudging technician who might as well have been hooking carpets as anything else.

In the hullabaloo that followed his first concert, when the likes of Igor dared no longer pass the city gates for fear of comparison to the French prodigy, David wisely followed my advice and developed a reputation as the youngest recluse in the business. Had you not been swept away to be married to Sarah, my guess is that you might have signed David on to the circuit then and there, robbing him of important years of study and self-discovery. In a biography like yours, a subject's personal idiosyncrasies are held up as foolproof indications of genius; the mere fact that David gave no interviews and refrained from public performance is sufficient evidence of his supreme artistic gifts. Never mind that these decisions were taken by me and by David's parents.

Politics have always been central to your work and public utterances – and never more pointlessly since your knighthood took the pressure off. Today you adopt the ideologically sound stances that I gather are *de rigueur* in your social circles, to the extent that a ten-year-old boy who rarely looked up from the keyboard was suddenly *'caught up in the upheavals that rocked late-Sixties France.'*

> *Cobblestones flew over barricades through the tear-gas and bounced at the centipede feet of de Gaulle's storm-troopers. Youth had taken the streets. It was a time of questioning, of re-evaluation, and the most satisfying of all the youthful political movements of the Sixties.*

It was a time of bloody-minded hooliganism, if you ask me, and successful only if you can look at France today and see a place much changed. Many of my own friends were caught up in these outrages against public order; they would meet me at the Père et Fils late at night, their eyes streaming from the tear-gas, and talk about the day's fighting as if they had played in a rugby match.

Your book leads one to believe that David took to the streets and risked his precious hands hurling stones and overturning cars: if political activism is inseparable from art, or so your argument seems to run, to be an artist the child simply *had* to be political. I am trying to imagine David at twelve, in a leather jacket and motorcycle boots, a yellow Gauloise glued to his lower lip, a picture of Che above the piano, attending secret meetings with Johnny the Red, clenching his little fist and shrieking Third World-related inanities in the company of braless women. This would be at odds with the first photograph of David in your book – uncredited; *I* took it – from around this time. Seated at my piano, wearing his school uniform, David gazes into the camera with all the revolutionary fervour of Tsar Nicholas II. If you look closely, you will see that the book in David's hands is my own ancient edition of Bach's Forty-eight – signed by Chopin himself, by the way, which would have made an interesting caption to the photograph – not the Communist Manifesto. I had been trying to keep David away from Bach's music for as long as possible, the danger being that once under the master's spell he would never deign to play anything else. So while you witter on about David's *'political psyche'* being *'forged in the crucible* (sic) *of revolutionary Paris'*, what we had in fact was a child coming to grips with the far more important matter of absolute compositional mastery.

Bach's keyboard works had so profound an effect on David that I am surprised you do not mention this phase, especially as you had previously expressed so much concern about David's tendency to 'toy' with piano music. Bach put an end to those shenanigans, I assure you. I remember remarking to myself that David's physical features actually changed after a few weeks' exposure to the Forty-eight. I would have sworn that his eyes darkened, his mouth developed a thoughtful pout, his shoulders hunched slightly more than usual when he played, as if under the mighty weight of responsibility to Bach.

Because David liked my piano so much, he took his lessons at my house. Gabrielle and Chantal always stayed to say hello to him, then went off to a café to wait for us to finish. On Mondays David came by during his school lunch break. On Wednesdays he received special dispensation from his teachers to take the first two hours off in the morning. On Fridays he took the whole afternoon off for an open-ended lesson.

I suppose your readers were satisfied with your summation of David's tutelage – *'Just like your own childhood piano lessons, only more so'* – and if I had been consulted on the subject I fear my information would have been detailed and dull. But it *is* dull playing scales and arpeggios, picking over scores and fingerings, dragging out the blasted Czerny, sight-reading reduced orchestral pieces, grinding out transpositions to distant keys, the only relief coming when I suicidally relented to a game of chess. David practised morning and night, and all day on Saturday. On most Sundays his parents managed to wrest him away from the piano to drive him to their country cottage.

I have no doubt that if he had written his own memoirs, David might have romanticized this period in his life, as so many great musicians do. He might have told of going to the theatre with you, hearing his first piano concerto and nearly fainting with excitement. He might have told of his parents' loving support and interest. He might have told of my own sympathetic contribution. But, like you, he would not have told the truth. The truth is dull.

What is less boring – and I am so glad to see it occupying a full five pages of your book, at the expense of any dry description of David's life just before puberty – is your inclusion of what I suspect you consider to be a comic episode in my life. I am referring, of course, to the Claudia Resputani fiasco, which in your blasé style you distort appallingly. Your readers will now believe that, twelve months after my wedding, I was found out in an extra-marital affair so inconceivably humiliating that I felt compelled to live outside France for several months afterwards.

You have rendered the two main characters in a way approaching the factual: Rafael Resputani, an Italian friend of mine from Conservatoire days, who had made the grave mistake of marrying money; and Claudia, the money he married, who was a horrid woman of fifty-odd (I shiver when I think of her jagged green teeth, her drooling, twisted mouth, her rasping, malodorous breath). Rafael, seeing the light at last, decided to extricate himself from this thoroughly unpleasant union, and to enlist my services in expediting their separation. The first I heard about this was Rafael's breathless telephone call from his local café, where he must have stood at the copper bar in front of a brandy, clutching a fistful of *jetons*.

'Pierre,' he said, 'I can take no more of Claudia.'

79

I told him that I was sorry, but not surprised.

'Another man would be happy with his mistress,' he said, 'and grit his teeth at home.'

'It has been known,' I agreed.

'This will not do in my case. Claudia is demanding and insatiable.' We were speaking in Italian, and my wrist would go numb if I attempted to write down even a small part of what Rafael said on this subject. 'In short,' he said at last, 'I need your help. I have a plan.'

'Just a moment, Rafael,' I said, jumping to conclusions. 'You are a good friend. There are very few things I would not do for you in a pinch. But I am afraid that murder is not one of them.'

Rafael roared with anarchic laughter.

'Murder? My God, *murder*?'

'It has been known,' I said again.

'I have no wish to kill Claudia,' said Rafael. 'Well,' he added, as if considering the possibility for the first time, 'not physically *kill* her, no, I don't think so. And of course I would never ask you to become involved in such a . . . such a sordid affair.'

'How very good of you.'

'I believe my plan to be perfect,' said Rafael. 'It is an age-old solution to my problem – not original, I admit, but highly effective.'

'I am listening.'

'Do you remember the last time you saw Claudia?' he asked me.

With some distaste I searched my mind for my last glimpse of Rafael's wife.

'That would have been the night of David's concert. We met in the lobby. Correct?'

'That's it!' shouted Rafael. 'Yes!'

'We just said hello, as I recall. She was among David's well-wishers.'

'Yes! But what I want to say is, she spoke to me in a most uncharacteristic way that night, when we went to a restaurant after the boy's performance. She may have drunk even more than usual. Do you want to know what she said to me?'

'I suppose so.'

'She said, "That Pierre La Valoise," she said. She said, "That Pierre, he must be the most sensual man I know." *Sensual*, my friend.'

'How kind of her.'

'She adores you!'

'But Rafael, that was such a long time ago.'

'Oh, she has mentioned you very frequently. No, she feels very strongly.'

'I have a horrible feeling I know what you're driving at.' I was lying in bed with Gabrielle at the time; I believe Chantal had gone out for cigarettes.

'Perhaps you do,' said Rafael, even more excitedly. Another *jeton* clicked into the slot. 'This is it. I want you to be discovered in the arms of Claudia. This would solve all of my problems. You are the only man who could do this for me. She loves me, but I am convinced she would be susceptible to the attractions of a man like you. I have purchased the most remarkable German camera, and I could . . . '

'Don't you think, Rafael,' I said, with Gabrielle nuzzling my neck and drawing one of her fingers along the inside of my quivering thigh, 'don't you think that what you are asking me to do is slightly, oh, *undignified*, under the circumstances?'

There was a brief silence on the other end of the line as Rafael considered how best to go about convincing me. He had given up a hopeless career as a violinist to become an even more hopeless, if lovable, lawyer. Persuasion was not his strong suit.

'Pierre, my friend,' he said, abandoning any logical line and resorting to pitiful supplication, 'you simply must help me.'

I do not know why I said yes. Perhaps it was out of loyalty to Rafael, but I doubt it. I think it had more to do with Gabrielle's irresistible attentions, and her annoyance at not being able to understand Italian, that made me tell Rafael I would do what he asked, and put down the telephone.

It is likely that I thought Rafael was drunk, and that I would never hear him speak to me on the subject again. If that was the case, then I miscalculated badly: a weekday night the following month found me being entertained in Claudia's drawing room. Rafael was supposedly far away, on business in Quebec, but was in fact waiting around the corner with his camera, preparing a surprise entrance. The fact that Rafael had never before been invited or sent abroad on 'business' did not seem to raise Claudia's suspicions.

You take gleeful pleasure in describing for your readers how hideous Claudia was, physically, and how unbearable it was to be subjected to her personality. For once your attempts at exaggeration failed, for one could never write about the experience of sitting across from an amorous Claudia without living it first hand.

As instructed, I arrived at the Resputani house looking my most debonair and seductive, bearing flowers and wine, only to be greeted by Claudia at her most gorgonian. She had used part of the gigantic fortune that had attracted Rafael in the first place, to purchase some examples of the latest fashions: the kind of clothes the rest of us scoff at in magazines, wondering who in her right mind would wear such monstrosities. Claudia, in her right mind or not, was one of those people. On the night in question she wore, or held up off the ground with her body, a shimmering curtain composed of green plastic squares connected by elastic bands. She had entrusted her grotesque head of hair to a visionary sculptor who seemed not to mind that passers-by would take his creation for a fright wig: two pointed wings of dyed ochre sprang from a dense, oblate skull-cap of a slightly lighter hue; at the back of her head, two horse-tail falls were attached to the main structure with leather thongs. On another occasion my reaction would have been one of pity for a middle-aged woman so misguided in her attempts to remain young and beautiful that she actually made matters far worse, and sadness at the idea that she thought such a transformation possible in the first place.

I greeted her with warm kisses, and although I deliberately exhaled through my nostrils as I did so, her perfume – no, perfume is the wrong word, her *odour* – leaked into my senses. I suppose the outermost scent had reacted badly with one of the inner layers of cream and makeup she had applied, but the result was as if a team of military scientists had laboured long years to arrive at the one substance that would cause instant distress in a man. I raised my bouquet of flowers between us as a fragrance shield, only to have it snatched away from me by one of Claudia's taloned hands. She led me by the arm to an ornate love seat, as if dispensing with formalities and addressing herself to my masculinity before Rafael could be psychically warned and return in time to discover us.

My arrangement with Rafael was that I would endeavour partially to unclothe his wife within half an hour of my arrival, and that he would burst in upon us before I was compelled to come in further contact with Claudia. I cannot claim any mastery of seduction in this case, for I read in Claudia's fake-lashed, almost arachnoid eyes a torrid desire that, quite frankly, panicked me. As she sat down next to me her dress made a startling noise. She handed me a glass of champagne and ravenously toasted my presence.

'Pierre,' she purred – and I use the hackneyed verb advisedly: eighty or ninety Turkish cigarettes a day had scarred and scoured her throat, much as it had given her breath an odour of corruption that her obvious dental decay alone could not account for. 'I have waited years to see you alone.'

'Claudia,' I said, non-committally. That was all I had expected to have to say during the course of my ordeal.

'Pierre,' she repeated with a sigh. 'Are we being naughty?' She feigned a guilty pout.

'Claudia,' I said.

'Oh, we are, we are,' said Claudia, and I could see that the woman was about to kiss me. Having lost all judgement of time, I blocked her attempt by raising my forearm between us and looking at my wristwatch. I had been in Claudia's drawing room for fifty seconds.

I confess that I wanted desperately to leave, to abandon Claudia to the agony of her husband's abrupt and meaningless return. I wonder if anyone who has met Claudia would believe me when I say that after the first excruciating minutes on her love seat I began to feel such pity for this preposterous and very ugly woman that I resigned myself to playing my role and flattering her. Admittedly her pleasure would be short-lived, for I had come to disembarrass her of her husband, but I wanted to make the best of unfortunate circumstances.

I also wanted the time to pass more quickly. Having fended off her first lunge and regained the defensive prop of my champagne glass, I tried to lend to my features the expression of a man who longs to hear the latest gossip, *all* the latest gossip, before succumbing to the implacable needs of the flesh. Because we knew practically no one in common aside from Rafael – and Claudia had no desire even to mention her husband's name – she soon abandoned small talk and took my free hand in hers. She held and stroked my hand, giving me the opportunity to study with amazement the slow clicks of the second hand on my wristwatch.

Another retreat to the champagne, a few more caresses of my hands and knees, and twenty minutes had elapsed. It was time to arrange a scene of *delicto* in which to be caught *flagrante*.

'Oh, darling,' she said, in mock surprise, as I leaned forward and put my arms around her shoulders. I still believed I could bring the deception to its unhappy conclusion without actually kissing Claudia. To this end I pretended to nuzzle Claudia's neck, all the while exploring the back of her laughable plastic dress for a means to its removal. This inflamed Claudia. The more she tried to pry my head away in order to kiss my dry and tightly puckered mouth, the harder I had to force my face into her neck and fright-wig, which she interpreted as evidence of my fierce but guilt-ridden ardour.

I was getting nowhere with the plastic dress, working blind and unfamiliar with the modern technology of couture. I decided that Claudia would quickly solve the riddle for me if I relented and allowed her to kiss me. I steeled myself, back there in the tangles of her 'hair', then began pecking at her neck and jaw with about as much force and mouth-work as a feeding tropical fish. Claudia moaned and arched her back, of course. I cringed, but carried on. I had only minutes to spare. I nosed through the layers of her cream and powder, located her tacky lips, and kissed her as chastely as I considered commensurate with my desire for her to undress. I felt her body heave and palpitate, which caused a considerable amount of plastic noise.

'Let's go to the bedroom,' said Claudia.

'No.' Now I had to pretend that my lust had grown so intense that it had to be seen to its glorious climax without the slightest interruption. I made groaning noises and returned to the neck-nuzzling stalling tactic. A glance at my watch over her shoulder told me the time had come. Rafael would crash through the doors, flash-bulbs blazing, in less than a minute.

'Claudia,' I gasped. 'Let me see you.' I made it clear that I meant she ought to remove her dress.

Claudia's dress had a secret catch somewhere, which she slipped one-handed. The dress came away like a deflated life-raft.

Claudia had gone to great expense equipping herself with undergarments. It pains me to resurrect the image of the pale, freckled folds of her bosom contrasting with the oily-black silk of her elaborate brassiere.

'I want to see you,' I repeated, just to get rid of this horrid garment and save myself the crucial seconds that would have been wasted had I tried to detach it on my own.

Claudia expertly unlatched the brassiere at the front, so that it sprang away from her body and lashed at my nearby cheek. I clasped my hands over what was revealed, more than anything to remove them from my sight. Claudia responded alarmingly. I clasped and nuzzled and held on for dear life, for the moment of truth was upon us. I focused my thoughts on the sound of Rafael's key in the latch.

Claudia, meanwhile, decided that she was in need of contact with what she had undoubtedly heard was my awesome virility. Her false nails tripped along my thigh in the direction of what was, I can assure you, a reluctant – no, an *ashamed* private part. It is an indication of man's absolutely insane pride that it occurred to me that I might be humiliated if Claudia discovered my complete lack of arousal

– my *anti*-arousal – my wholesale *retreat*, on the arousal front. There were two avenues open to me, therefore: to crush her hand between my knees and prevent further progress; or somehow to trick myself into unwanted manfulness. I chose the latter course.

I forced out all thoughts of the key in the door, and thought instead of my dear new wife, Gabrielle. She had never failed me before, after all. It occurred to me at the time that this was an ironic opposite of one's juvenile mental calculating of dull statistics or repulsive images in order to forestall orgasm. The desired result, I am happy to report, was swiftly achieved, so that rapturous Claudia was spared the brutal disappointment of a man half her age unresponsive to her touch.

'Come *on*, Rafael,' I thought, one thousand times per second. 'Come *on*.'

When Rafael did not come – and when Claudia showed all the signs of being on the verge of doing so – I had to admit to myself that I was no longer an actor in a wicked drama; I was making love to Claudia. You may interpret my decision to carry on in any way you wish, but I like to think I did the gentlemanly thing. We rolled on to the floor between the love seat and the low drinks table, and there the act was soon in progress. I must say that I found this to be rather stimulating, which says a great deal for a man's capacity to gain pleasure in unexpected places, but I did worry still that Rafael would return, a quarter of an hour late, to photograph what had become a full–blown carnal event.

The important fact – and I admit this only to highlight the manner in which history is distorted by grandiose recall – is that I was honestly transported by my enforced union with Claudia. This does not mean I was not appalled when I opened my eyes and beheld her in the steaming afterglow. Still, I survived the ordeal on a wave of pride in having acted at the last minute in poor Claudia's interest. I had made a tragic woman happy, which mitigated any pre- or post-coital suffering on my part.

My exit was not difficult to justify. 'What have we done?' I said, slapping a palm to my forehead. 'My God! Rafael!

My friend . . . ' That sort of thing. I was on the pavement outside Claudia's house within minutes, pretending to race despairingly into the night.

I wanted to find Rafael and punish him. I searched the neighbourhood and asked café waiters if they had seen him. He had not waited in the pre-arranged place, that much I was able to ascertain. I did at last discover from one of Rafael's cronies at the 'Bar-Bar' bar, that Rafael had of late begun to frequent the flat of a Mademoiselle Martineau in the rue de Grenelle. After consulting a phone directory, I made my way there.

In effect, then, it was *I* who burst in upon an illicit sexual affair. In his guilt, craven Rafael had retreated to the safety of his mistress's bed, leaving me to my own devices in Claudia's arms. Is such a thing forgivable? I thought not. I decided to thrash my friend Rafael on the premises. Mademoiselle Martineau – in her own way even less attractive than Claudia, in my opinion – looked on as I dribbled Rafael around her drawing room like a football. She called the police. I was arrested. Rumours of my affair with Claudia began to circulate. My violence was taken to be the result of a confrontation with my secret lover's husband. I fled the country with Gabrielle and Chantal, who found the story so amusing that they spoke of nothing else for the three months we stayed – with you – in England.

I was happy to be away. I conducted David's thrice-weekly lessons over the telephone, which he greatly enjoyed. Gabrielle, Chantal and I stayed in the west wing of Dollsworthy, while you and Sarah occupied the east. Your mother, who rather liked me, spent most of her time in the London house.

Living in a state of disgrace and exile, La Valoise came to stay with me and my then wife, in England. The closer scrutiny of his personality afforded by his visit did much to assuage my fears that David's progress might be hindered by the complex Frenchman's influence. I

tried to put my prejudices aside – no small feat since La
Valoise had arrived with two women, only one of them
his wife – and look at the man with a new objectivity.
In the evenings, when he played the piano for us, I
saw the artist behind the madman. His playing was
gloriously lush, and all the more poignantly affecting
for its having sprung from the heart of a thoroughly
ruined personality. I dare say even David at his best
never quite moved me the way La Valoise did on those
cherished evenings at Dollsworthy.

Geoffrey, I am sincerely touched.

I had been dabbling in composition at the time, and
I marvelled at the Frenchman's ability to reduce and
play at sight my rather sloppily copied manuscripts. I
found it quite encouraging when he expressed admira-
tion for my work. A composer, no matter how confident
– and I was anything but confident! – always yearns for
his colleagues' approval.

I am glad I left you with this memory of my reaction to your
'music', but think for a moment: I was a guest in your stately
home; your face as you anticipated what I might say was like a
small child's; your wife was in the room. What did you expect
me to say? If only your readers could know that the piece you
are describing here was a score for ten strings, sounded like
Elgar on a damaged turntable, and was dedicated to the Duke
of Marlborough.

Your one concession to the era was to torture your regal
tune with frenetic, itchy-sounding and utterly random comments from the accompanying parts. I used to write music
like that at the Conservatoire when I was fifteen, except that
I didn't bother with the regal melody and stuck altogether to
the feculent grumblings beneath. (*Why*, the future will ask of
us, did people feel they had to create such things?) You would
toil away on your composition – gazing out on your ancestral
lands and thinking that England *was* lovely, after all. Then you

would pop downstairs for a sherry and some tear-shedding as I played a snatch of Schumann for you, knowing that what you had committed to paper that afternoon was a deliberate corruption of the music you supposedly loved. I find it hard to believe that the Duke of Marlborough was impressed, but I gather flattery was the main thing.

Having said that, I must return the compliment you paid me in the section just quoted. My stay at Dollsworthy made me believe that you were in many ways an honourable and sincere person. I would never hold bad music against a composer – not these days. Music needs a messiah, but in his absence people like you must potter along, go through the motions, try to preserve your dignity as you invent new words to label the noises you make. I remember one evening when the women had gone to bed and we were discussing your 'composition', and I said in all seriousness that you and others like you were 'driving a stake into the heart of European music.' You took this as a compliment.

We had some fun, too, didn't we? Sarah was always worth a laugh or two, when her medications were mixing properly. As horribly as your first marriage turned out, I don't suppose you regret having lived for a few years with what we politely call a 'free spirit'. I have never had an insane wife, and in many ways I envy you the experience. I guess little Emanuel was around somewhere, but you kindly never exposed him to your guests. You were the consummate host, which is all the more surprising to me when I think how difficult it must have been for you to sleep under the same roof with Gabrielle. How you must have longed for just ten seconds of her mouth's attention.

In short, I returned to Paris thinking quite fondly of you, and believing that together we might see David – our hobby, our experiment, my friend – to terrific heights. It was a letdown, therefore, to discover upon my return that David had decided never to play again.

David sat on my couch with his bare legs crossed, drinking a cup of tea. I played at child psychology.

'Quite right,' I said. 'Silly thing, the piano. You've made the right decision, I'm sure of it. Too *hard*, really, for a boy to play well. Not worth it. Leave it to others.'

'Right,' said David, and slurped his tea.

He had grown noticeably during my exile, but still looked thin and fragile for a boy of thirteen.

'But I'd just like to know something. I spoke to you on the phone just last week – we went through our little lesson as usual. What happened to change your mind?'

David shrugged his shoulders and blew out his cheeks.

'Was it something you played? Something you didn't like to play?' I was afraid that Bach might have intimidated him.

'No.'

'Were you bored? It can all be very boring.'

'No.'

'Maybe you were trying something terribly difficult and new – and because I wasn't there . . . You haven't been playing the Liszt Sonata again, have you?'

'No.'

'Any pain or stiffness in your arms or wrists or hands?'

David held up his free right hand and wiggled his fingers. 'No.'

'It's not really important, of course,' I said, 'but I'm curious. Can you tell me what happened?'

'I think so.'

'Take your time.'

David put down his teacup. He sighed in his girl's voice.

'Oh,' he said, 'it is very simple.'

'Yes?'

'I had a vision.'

'Ah, a *vision*.' This was not what I had expected to hear. One has to be so careful with geniuses. 'What was the vision? Was it a dream? A nightmare, perhaps?'

'No, I said a vision. While I was playing, something spoke to me. It was a deep voice, and I saw its face in the music.'

'What did it look like?'

David thought for a moment.

'It looked a little like Mister Brahms.'

Oh, no, I thought. He's seen God. There was always a danger that an otherwise well-brought-up boy could become religious. They picked up such things in school, like influenza. Some of my friends had complained of the problem.

'So the man had a big beard?'

'It wasn't a man,' said David. 'It was a vision.'

'Quite right. So you said. Do you remember what it said?'

'Yes. The first thing it said was "Hello, David." '

'That makes sense, I suppose. A polite vision that knew your name.'

'Yes. Then it said, "David, you are going to die." '

'What a horrible thing for a vision to say.'

'Yes. I was still playing, so I didn't say anything back. I was frightened.'

'I can imagine that you were. Did the vision say anything else?'

'Yes. It said, "What you are doing is of no use." '

'How awful.'

'Yes. It said, "Stop it straightaway." '

'And you took that to mean that you should stop playing the piano?'

'Yes. It seemed perfectly clear. It frightened me, but when I stopped playing, the vision disappeared.'

'This is very alarming.'

'Yes.'

'But you ought to be happy that you had a vision. *I've* never had a vision.' This was untrue. A vision of sorts had ended my career in the Salle Thierry.

'It wasn't at all pleasant,' said David.

'I suppose you are thinking that if you play again, the vision will return. By not playing you avoid any more threats.'

'Yes. It makes sense, no?'

'Yes indeed.'

Caution was called for on my part. My philosophy regarding David had always been that he should never be told that music was in any way *compulsory*. If you think about it in the broadest sense, this is true enough. Music is a luxury, and like all luxuries it sometimes exacts an irrational premium. The price in the performer's case is hardship, uncertainty, and in my case and David's a slice of sanity. I assumed that what David had experienced – his 'vision' – was no more than a first existential pang. All children must have them, but most children run outside and play with their friends or beat up their siblings instead of associating their cosmic discomfort with music. David had little else in his life, so it is not surprising that a Brahms-like figure spoke to him rather than the stars, the night, the mountains, or other catalysts of angst. My immediate task was to convince David that his mortality was unconnected to his art, but casuistry had never been my strong suit.

'It won't be the last time you feel this way,' I told him. 'But it would be worth your while, when you are in the mood, to give the piano a try again. You could play mine, right now, if you liked. See it there? What a beautiful sight. If you look hard enough you can almost hear it being played. If you look very hard indeed you can almost hear Mister Brahms playing it, can't you?'

David and I looked at my great Bösendorfer with its lion's–paw feet. I hoped that David would understand my point, that the piano, like life, made even less sense than usual in the absence of a person to play or live it. If his little *crise* was partly musical and partly existential, I thought the analogy might serve at least to inspire him into activity. Not that it really mattered, of course. I already lived under the weight of my own disillusionment: music no longer made order of the world for me; in fact, it did the opposite. I would not have been the first to announce that music had died, but this was no intellectual posturing on my part. It was a negative and visceral emotion, like a permanent depression. Like the polite atheist who silently looks on incredulously, so to speak, as a fellow man cloaks himself in faith, I kept my own musical counsel and wished all others luck. With hindsight I can say that deep inside I hoped David would rekindle my musical belief.

We sat in silence for a few minutes. My grandfather's grandfather clock beat time like a metronome set on larghetto. David tapped his fingers on his knees. At last David sucked in his lips, then expelled a blubbing sigh.

'It really would be a shame,' he said, 'if there were no one to play the thing.'

We were back in business. For all I know, David's brief spell of self-doubt was merely a hormonal overload. He grew rapidly and no longer looked adults in the eye, but at least he practised. I spent most of our lessons talking to him about school, about friends, about girls. His teachers adored him and had to deliver confidential letters to Henri and Camille describing the ways in which standard grading scales were insufficient to express their child's academic excellence. There was talk of removing David from school and sending him to a private tutor, if only to spare his classmates galling comparisons. I advised David's parents to veto any suggestion of skipping grades or private tutelage on the basis that any social contact with children his age could only be a grounding influence. The major decision we made during this period was that David would be kept out of music schools, especially my Conservatoire, perhaps forever.

> *I was astonished to learn of La Valoise's insistence that David not apply to one of the world's most prestigious conservatoires. I made a special trip to Paris to debate the issue with him and with David's parents. I told them of my own experiences as a youth, of the great pleasure I took in the company of fellow young musicians. Would David, I asked them, benefit in the same way at a conventional school, surrounded by normal children who shared none of his interest or talent in music?*

I made short work of your arguments, I'm sure you will agree: David was already head and shoulders above the most accomplished children even five years his senior; musicians tend to be maladjusted, nervous, spotty, practical-joking, over-protected, jealous and male; he already had, I thought, the best teacher in Europe; music-school children do not get enough exercise.

Your last-ditch argument was that without a certificate from one of the world's acclaimed institutions, David might be left behind. I countered that we would see who was left behind when David won the Gaston-Robert Competition at the age of fifteen, leaving conservatoires full of Igors in his wake. I had grown somewhat confident of his skills, you see. You returned to Dollsworthy and your increasingly unstable wife and child, more uncertain than ever of your role.

I was more uncertain than ever of my role in David's career.

Here is the first occurrence of the word 'career' in your book, describing the piano-playing of a fourteen-year-old boy. In other words, by implication, we have now graduated in your text to the professional period in David's *Life*, which lasted until his *Death*. I recall pausing at this stage in your narrative, knuckles white on my chair's arm rests, visualizing my own aborted book. This is about the point where I abandoned it, having decided that a mere sentence would be as accurate: David Debrizzi, born Paris, 1956, by age fourteen played the piano rather well.

What follows in your *Life*, and David's, is worthy of closer scrutiny – I know this perhaps better than you suspect. But when I turned the page and read 'Part Two: The Good Years', I thought I would gag on my illicit brandy. The Good Years, indeed.

Your

PART TWO

❚❚ ❚❚❚ ❚

THE GOOD

YEARS

Your
CHAPTER FIVE

> *Having recently separated from my wife and made my
> secondary home in Paris, I was able to spend more time
> than ever with David. I had begun devoting more of
> my energies to composition, and found my weekly hour
> with David to be a most diverting sideline.*

I am so glad you were enjoying yourself.

> *It is a happy coincidence that I alighted in Paris when
> I did, for La Valoise was going through another bad
> patch and was quite unable to fulfill his regular duties
> with anything like the dedication David and I required
> of him. Poor fellow, La Valoise had discovered that he
> was unable to father children. He mooned about for
> months until Gabrielle, his wife, saw no alternative
> but to leave him. I don't know if I have ever seen so
> depressed a young man . . .*

Well, Geoffrey, you should see me right now. You mention
my sterility no less than eighteen times from this point on.
You must have been thrilled to land on so handy a metaphor

for what you saw as my more profound failings. You make it quite clear that you suspect my infertility must be due to long bouts of venereal disease, possibly many strains acting in concert, ganging up on my testicles and wringing the life out of them. My doctor could have told you that my sterility – which you erroneously call 'impotence' at least once – was congenital, so to speak, and my two brief spells of gonorrhoea had nothing whatsoever to do with it.

As to your conclusion that Gabrielle 'left' me because I was a biological cul-de-sac, your lazy stab at the truth misses once again the heart of the matter: Gabrielle and I both wanted her to marry someone else, an old American friend of my step-mother's. Under French law, as elsewhere, we had to divorce and annul in order to make Gabrielle's second marriage legally and socially acceptable; the no-issue issue did not bear on our decision. I can happily report that Gabrielle became a grandmother just last year.

And where was David during all of our marital and pro-creative turmoil? Sitting at the piano, as usual. At fifteen he was quite tall and slender, but lacked the awkwardness usually attached to that build. He bore up well under the mild pressure of his renown, and learned early and forever not to take his talent too seriously. He set about his pianistic chores as he had always done, sedulously and without complaint.

His evident physical beauty was another matter entirely. He was old enough to attend my dinner parties, and he revelled in the attention of my women friends. You insist on using the adjectives that were suitable for describing a good-looking little boy, when what David had already become was a powerful erotic magnet attracting all women and girls who neared. I know because they told me so. David would leave one of my dinners, and as soon as the door closed behind him the women would collapse in histrionic sighs of longing or regret. They thought he exuded a hard but romantic air of Corsican mystery.

One thing you will probably have noticed in life is how far good looks will advance a person, not least in fields like music where one would have thought them irrelevant.

I have adjudicated dozens of instrumental competitions in my day, and I freely admit that the lissome flautist, the tawny harpist, the sharp-jawed trumpeter – all have profited from my susceptibility to physical attractiveness. I make no excuses except to say that charisma lends mystique to art, and superficial appearances give an instant leg-up to any performance. All of this certainly heightens one's admiration for some of the wretches on today's concert circuit who have had to overcome the unalterable.

David had no such problem. He was beautiful. He was graceful. He spoke rarely, and always with a bashful, winning grin. At fifteen he was fully aware of his attractiveness to girls, and he was self-possessed enough to want to put it to use at the earliest opportunity. It is no surprise that he came to me for advice.

I have to say that my earliest anxieties concerning La Valoise's potentially corrupting influence were more than vindicated by his reckless way of speaking frankly to David on the subject of sex.

Well, it isn't as if I embarked on a sex-education course, taking the parents' or the state's role into my hands, is it? There was nothing obscene nor prurient nor even controversial in what I told David. He certainly knew what was supposed to go where, and I like to think he came to me for the more romantic embellishments that his parents were too shy to discuss, and his friends too naïve to comprehend. It was rather like my advice to David before his first concert, when I told him he might actually *enjoy* what others told him he should fear. I shudder to think what you might have told him – or not told him – about sex, had he come to you. Your readers will not know that you bring up this quite trivial topic only to lay deeper and stronger foundations for your attacks on me in chapters to come.

The only way biography will ever work properly, I fear, is if everyone is wired for sound and pictures at birth. To read or see the perfect biography of a future Napoleon or Wagner,

99

the scholar will have to spend a lifetime glued to a monitor and speakers, unable to conduct a life of his own. He will emerge, in old age, knowing *exactly* what happened, but, ironically, incapable of passing on what he has learned without committing the same offences as conventional biographers. Had David been equipped with microphone and camera during the instance at hand, you and your audience would have seen and heard me giving him a jolly little talk about love and flesh, in which I told him what a marvellous time he was going to have with girls. It was as simple as that.

'You are going to have a marvellous time with girls,' I said to him. I may have used facial expressions to stress how much I believed this to be the case, but I did not go into much verbal detail on the subject.

Next time David saw you he must have repeated my prediction, which you then magnified in your own mind to such proportions that David's mystified parents were once again called in to censure me. And now, two decades on, after plenty of time to mull over this microscopically insignificant event in your subject's life, you feel compelled to draw Jacqueline into the equation.

> *Evidently La Valoise considered himself to be the victim of a cosmic injustice. An early girlfriend – perhaps even a fiancée – a promising flautist named Jacqueline Arrand, had died. La Valoise seemed to use this tragic fact as an excuse for all his future misbehaviour, and expected unquestioning sympathy from those of us who were in a position to criticize his excesses.*

It is a shame that duelling has gone out of style. Several of my ancestors have attested to its effectiveness, and even without experience I believe I could give a spindly-armed Englishman a run for his money. You have succeeded here in portraying me as self-pitying and immature, of having inflated or romanticized my sense of loss, and of heartlessly referring all my future social victims to a formative calamity of, in your opinion, dubious importance.

This is frustrating. Much as I would like to lay claim to a transcendent love for Jacqueline, in fact I had long since recovered my equilibrium. I told you the story of that episode in my life, during my 'exile' at Dollsworthy. I remember drawing tortured analogies between music and love, and comparing Jacqueline's death to the demise of my piano career. While I meant most of what I said, I find it hard to believe that you thought I meant I would never fall in love again, when my *wife* was in the room.

If nothing of much importance was happening in David's life, the same could not be said of Igor Malechievich. In the summer of 1972, Igor and Boris and several hangers-on fetched up in a safe house in Washington having thrown themselves on the mercy of the United States Government. It was no time at all before father and son were photographed beside the maniacal American president who even then, unbeknownst to his valued Communist defectors, had set his own ruin in train. Suitable statements were issued from the Malechievich camp on the intolerably repressive regime they had left behind, on the sense of sadness defectors feel after taking the irrevocable leap (and leaving family at home), on the gratitude they felt towards their new capitalist sponsors. Life, they said, warmly shaking the President's hand, was much, *much* better in the United States, if presidential banquets were any comparison to go by.

I mention this momentous change in Igor's life mainly because you chose to parrot the standard line, which is that the teenaged Russian's courageous escape lent a certain weight to his subsequent performances, especially at Carnegie Hall, and a poignancy to his public utterances of loneliness so far away from the steppes. You might have added that within two weeks of Igor's arrival in America a television programme had dressed him in a cowboy outfit, playing a medley of kitsch 'classical' tunes in a setting of haystacks and wheat-sucking Southern belles. Igor managed to retain his sourest expression beneath his ten-gallon hat, wearing overalls and a checked shirt, and millions of Americans witnessed the moving moment when, after prolonged canned applause, young Igor pronounced his first words in English: 'God bless America.' It was a far cry from the Tchaikovsky Concert Hall, but who can scoff at hard currency?

We were cautiously elated at these developments, and at the prospect of Igor's self-immolation in the land of the free. We tried to remind ourselves that musical performance bore no relation to competitive sport, all the while sniggering into our espressos at the thought of Igor's prostituting his talents to the hideous dollar. We shared a view, I suspect, that all things American were antipathetic to art, little knowing what magnificent music those supposedly evil dollars would buy.

Igor's indecently lucrative Principal record contract, struck when the Russian was still sixteen, took us by surprise. Lucky Igor struck early gold. The Americans had figured out how to take a little boy, dress him up in foreign ethnic dress, all but ignore the skill for which he had become famous, pander to nationalism, and at the same time make it seem somehow justifiable merely by conferring sudden wealth upon the victim. They even convinced *me*, once I heard how much money they planned to pay Igor, and I had half a mind to undergo hypnotic therapy in order to be able to play again and get my part of the action. Needless to say, Boris was a happy man.

David's next step was to be more conventional and less – shall we say – in keeping with the times. David would enter a competition. David would lay a substantial bit of his future on the line at one performance. His short-term fate would rest in the hands of a small panel of judges bleary-eyed from watching a procession of young pianists banging out their Schubert, their Beethoven, their Mozart, their Bach; their Prokofiev, their Scriabin, their Schumann, their Trunck; their Debussy, their Rachmaninov, their Scarlatti, their Grieg – all of this music so utterly *known* as to have been genetically passed on from father to son.

My God, how I hate the very *idea* of formal musical competitions. They amount to a human-rights violation, in my view, to say nothing of musical rights. And when they involve children, it is a sight I can only hope future generations will look back on as we do human sacrifice and other barbarities of relatively recent times. I feel more justified than most in holding this rather extreme opinion, because as a lad I entered three major competitions, and won all three quite handily. At the ages of twelve, fourteen and sixteen I took to the boards and slashed away at the keys just as my teachers had told me to do. I kept my head up and I rolled my eyes and I gave every external impression of being entirely in control of the music I played. Inside, like all the children I defeated, I was a quivering, confused, fatalistic wreck. How many times must we see the faces of children whose names are not called to the 'final' before we stop inflicting this torture upon them? The cameras are trained on the winners, of course, to spare us the sight of a teenager's hopes and dignity dashed. But you have been there, Geoffrey, and so have I. We have ourselves lowered the boom on these hapless youths, emerged from sequestered meetings like a hanging jury to read the list of 'winners'. I agreed to David's participation only in the certainty that he would win with ease.

The Gaston-Robert Competition was, and remains, the most prestigious piano contest in France for musicians under the age of nineteen. Your *Life* spares us all the interesting details and merely states that David Debrizzi walked away with the first prize, as if this were the foregone conclusion I had secretly predicted, and as if he had met no worthy opposition along the way. As always, there is more to the story than that.

David insisted that I alone accompany him to the competition, to keep the pressure at a minimum. We arrived at the vaguely Stalinist-looking Conservatoire near Montparnasse and there met Virginie, my new tuner and house guest. My previous tuner, a Belgian who went by the name of Hector, had been unfaithful to me: he had run off with a touring virtuoso, claiming that my sedentary Parisian life was not sufficiently glamorous for a man of his abilities. A more pleasant person than Hector, and an equally good tuner, Virginie also had the advantage of an ample appetite for the food I loved so much to cook. Hector had never really *believed* in my cooking, and needless to say I never invited him to share my home. My age or slightly older, shaped like a globe, ruddy of complexion, foul of mouth, hailing from Strasbourg, Virginie was all I could ever have asked for in a tuner and gastronome; she stayed with me for five years.

At the entrance to the Conservatoire, Virginie greeted us in a fury. The Gaston-Robert authorities had employed a tuner of their own, who wouldn't let her near David's piano. The tight schedule, he said, would not permit each contestant to fiddle with their allotted instruments.

'I told that little man,' Virginie said to us, breathless with irritation, 'that David was not just any other contestant, that to deny him his tuner was virtually to disqualify him, and that I would speak to his superiors. Naturally he said all the "parents" wanted the same thing, and he didn't care if he sabotaged the next Paderewski, and that if I didn't leave he would tune the piano backwards.'

'What a horrible experience for you, Virginie,' I said, warning with my eyes that David might be ruffled by her story. 'I'm certain that you had the last word.'

'I called him a pig and a pederast and a . . . '

'Well done. Did you check the piano?'

'Of course. Muddy, is what it is, and—' she looked at David, and decided to temper her appraisal, *'adequate.'*

'Everything is fine, then. Thank you, Virginie. Lead the way, if you will.'

Why is it, I ask you, that organizers of these events must always look so cold and officious? Such cleanly-parted hair, such dapper clothes, such pursed and knowing lips? We were taken into the care of one of these people, and led down the main staircase into a basement corridor resounding with a clash of piano-playing from the practice rooms. It sounded like one of Schumann's last insane auditory hallucinations, a hell of scales and rolls and trills. David covered his ears as we jogged through the aural barrage to the room marked 'D. Debrizzi'. The room brought back unpleasant memories of my years at the Conservatoire. Throughout the world these semi-sound-proofed rooms exist, with their chipped acoustic tiling, their yellowed piano keys, their cigarette-charred tables, their bent wire music stands – airless booths to dull the sound of mostly fruitless effort. On the small table in David's room lay a folder with his name written on its cover in authoritarian penmanship, containing an adhesive name-badge, legal waivers for me to sign, an itinerary – and an unwrapped chocolate mint stuck to the binding. Virginie opened her tool kit and spent ten minutes twisting the upright into a semblance of shape before I allowed David to noodle at its jaundiced keys.

I sat in the corner of the room, smoking, watching David closely. His expression was suitably enigmatic, the way mine must have been fifteen years before when I sat in a similar room being appraised by Monsieur Presteron. He played a few warm, Beethovenian chord-progressions of his own invention, feeling the keys, mustering the blind focus one can only achieve when performance is imminent. He crossed his legs and adopted a posture you would never have countenanced. Under his breath he asked me to light him a cigarette, something else you would have forbidden. I did so, and handed it to him. He took a puff, then placed it in the brown groove burnt between two keys in the highest register: most pianists smoke right-handed.

Not being David's parent, I had watched him mature in frequent glimpses, like a dancer under a strobe light. I am told parents experience the sensation of seeing their children 'suddenly grown-up', which must be something like what I felt that day in the practice room. But because our relationship had been almost exclusively musical, mine was more a feeling of 'suddenly' looking at a musician, a peer, someone who could enlighten me. I could see by the way successive waves of anxiety, defiance, fatalism and humour played across his face, that he had reached an adult consciousness of his situation.

105

David stopped playing, picked up his cigarette, and began smoking in earnest (he would smoke more or less constantly from then on). He swivelled on the piano bench and looked at me as he had never quite done before – as a *partner*.

'So, Pierre,' he said, as if he were interviewing me for a job. 'What will it mean to you if I win?'

'Mean to *me*?' I smoked a few lungfuls of my own and tried to divine David's angle. 'If you win, well, I suppose to *me* it simply means more rigorous work, no? Onward and upward?'

'You sound like Mr Flynch now.'

'Yes, well, in his absence I thought . . .'

'No. Tell me what you really think. You've always been dead set against competitions. I've heard you.'

'True enough. But a necessary evil.'

'That isn't what you really think. Perhaps you're against . . . the whole thing?' David gestured at the piano.

'Impossible to say what I really think. I would have to know you . . . *perfectly*, to know what I really think.'

'You would need hindsight, that's what you are saying. You would have to see me in a few hours, or in a few years, when I have won or lost, to know what you really think about my being here in the first place.'

'That is one of life's inconveniences, David, you've put your finger on it.'

'You're being sarcastic, Pierre,' said David.

Just listen, will you, Geoffrey, to the way David spoke. I was nonplused, to say the least. I had heard fleeting phrases of this sort of thing, but there I sat staring at a rather sour-looking teenager, smoking, accusatory, minutes away from his most important performance to date.

'Young man,' I said sternly, playing for at least another hour's role as tutor and guardian, 'this is not the time for you to turn on me, to accuse me in this way. What if you were to address yourself to the music for a spell, and we'll talk about this over a drink later?'

'I'm going to win anyway,' he said, which caused my eyes to bulge. 'You know that. I simply thought you could say what you meant for a change. I see no need for you to protect me from anything any longer. I mean, who *are* these children showing up today? Have you *heard* any of them?'

Wonderful, I thought; egomania is a useful response to pressure.

'I don't know who they are and, no, I haven't heard any of them play. Let's warm up a bit before we crush them, shall we?'

David angrily flicked his cigarette into the corner of the cell, so that I was obliged to go over and stamp it out. By the time I returned to my seat, David had begun to warm up properly. I asserted my authority, put him through his paces, tried to set aside for a moment the tiny rebellion of a few minutes before. We had a jolly difficult piece of piano playing ahead of us.

Despite David's blithe dismissal of the opposition, I knew from experience that whoever they were, the teenagers up and down that fetid corridor could make their way with great competence through some of the repertoire's most challenging pieces. Unlike the seeded David Debrizzi, most of them had negotiated testing preliminary rounds. There was no sense ignoring the possibility that one of them might simply *nail* a piece on the day. Some wore unusual makeup or clothes, all had put in roughly the same hours as David, some had undoubtedly succeeded in bribing a judge or two.

In my experience there were several ways for a very good pianist, even a superb one like David, to reduce the odds: one was to simplify, simplify – to play a technically 'easy' and familiar work with such perfection that a superior technique was merely *implied*; another was to pander to nationalism by playing only French pieces; another was to intimidate trend-conscious judges by playing the works of living or even young composers; another was to throw caution and fad to the wind and tear off into the most difficult piece ever crammed on to staves. David and I had chosen to combine the second and last courses.

Chanat's *Death Spiral*, written in the composer's last, tubercular weeks, is, in my opinion, the apotheosis of gaudy, pyrotechnic pianism.

Legend has it, as I am sure I have told you, that Chanat's son, Emile, concerned that his father had not been heard composing upstairs at the piano for some hours, burst into the great virtuoso's study to find his father lying half in, half out of an open window. More important – at least once Chanat was found by his son to be alive, if terribly unwell – is what Emile discovered on the other side of the room: the piano keys, spattered with his father's coughed-up blood; and a similarly bestrewn manuscript on the stand – the *Death Spiral*. It is to be supposed that Chanat, a romantic to the last and believing himself on the verge of disappearance, forced himself to finish this work, coughing and retching grotesquely, then surprised himself by failing to die. He collapsed before he was able properly to defenestrate himself. Chanat lived a few more weeks in physical agony, and in the perhaps more painful knowledge that the *Death Spiral* stood no hope of being asterisked in music encyclopaedias as a successful musical suicide–note to mankind.

But what a piece the *Death Spiral* is. Ostensibly written in Chanat's favourite key of C-sharp minor, this one-movement work is themeless, programmatic, disorderly, and at first glance has nothing to recommend it except that it was written down by a fairly well-known virtuoso, and is bloody difficult to play. David and I were probably the only pianists alive to have bothered memorizing Chanat's sadistic work, whose virtual unplayability suggests that Chanat's death-throes message was that he had reached his own limit of technique and could continue no longer.

Needless to say, the *Death Spiral* is supremely ugly. David and I used to have laughing fits when we worked on it at my house, where the reluctant Bösendorfer cringed under the lashings of our hands. (For years, the name 'Chanat' was our byword for doomed over-reaching: if a friend's ambitious business went bankrupt, we would say '*Il a fait un Chanat*.')

David played the *Death Spiral* as well or better than I did. He approached it as a party piece, as an amusement. The famous chromatic quadruple-octave thirty-second-note runs fell beneath his fingers the way the competition played major scales. David had been able to pull off the nastier bits since he was eight years old – even then he had thought them wildly funny – and by the time we reached the Gaston–Robert Competition he had added the ingredients of mock-seriousness that would have the grey-faced adjudicators slavering.

'Yim, bobby-dobby-dobby dim-dum, yim,' sang David, in the soundproof cell, parodying Chanat's already ludicrous score. 'Dobby-dum, ya-pa-ya-pa-ya-pa DUM, ya-pa-ya-pa-ya-pa DUM, ya-pa diddy-diddy-diddy-diddy-diddy-diddy DUM pa-da DUM – piddledy diddledy piddledy diddledy, piddly-piddly-piddly ya-pa diddly ya-pa DUM!'

We were soon called to the auditorium by our fastidious warder. 'David,' I whispered, as we went out into the corridor, '*Fais pas un Chanat.*'

David was escorted to a waiting room. I took my place in the back of the small, gloomy auditorium where Virginie had saved me a seat.

'So far,' she said, with typical bluntness, 'they are shit.'

'The best go last, don't forget.'

Out came a girl wearing the requisite monochrome ersatz-silk gown and white shoes, her face a pitiful mask of fear and failed concentration. Bang went Prokofiev, boom went Liszt, crash went Chopin.

Out came a boy in blazer and tie, tall and stooped and bespectacled. He howled his Scriabin, hammered his Duchamps, hashed his Mozart.

Out came a boy in a white suit and overlong hair and a springing gait. Virginie claimed to have heard of him. What he had in flair he more than polluted with careless playing. Berg had never sounded odder. His wild Chopin mazurka was a 'Chanat' if I ever heard one.

Out came a thirteen-year-old girl, young enough not to be entirely flustered by the occasion, who played a beautiful

Debussy, a spiritual Schubert, and an almost annoyingly well-played Prelude and Fugue. She was cute, too. I began to fidget in my seat; Virginie had to hold my hand.

David, who went last of all, strolled on to the stage as if he had wandered there accidentally from the boulevard outside. One could sense by the audience's collective intake of breath that David was well known to all. His reclusiveness, deliberate or not, had done wonders for his reputation; no one had forgotten his playful début at the Salle Thierry, and expectations were high. Virginie had to punch my shoulder when I squeezed her hand too hard.

With a mannerism worthy of Igor Malechievich, David walked all the way around the piano, trailing a finger along its edge, like a pilot inspecting the wing of his aircraft before a flight. He sat down with a grunt and drew his hands through the hair over his ears. He eyed the keys with palpable anger, placed his right foot on the sustaining pedal, curled his left leg back beneath the padded bench. He had positioned himself six inches or so farther to the left than normal, the better to gain leverage on the thumb-and-forefinger trills that Chanat relied upon for low-register drama.

From the very first, hilarious measures of the *Death Spiral*, David had won the competition. He played with such authority and purpose that the judges, who had spent much of the previous performances jotting notes beneath white cones of reading light, leaned back in their chairs, took off their glasses, gazed ceilingward, generally surrendered to the predictability of David's feat. The last section of the *Death Spiral*, which sounds like the screams of several thousand lemmings falling towards the sea, he played with such conviction, however false, that Chanat himself would have dropped to his knees in awe. David filled the room with Chanat's preposterous noise, and became during those fifteen minutes the most promising pianist in France.

The judges spent ten minutes backstage trying to find suitable adjectives for their presentation of the grand prize. When finally they handed David his certificate, carefully stressing that *all* the competitors were worthy of the highest

110

possible praise, a row of photographers gathered to preserve the handshakes for posterity. The others packed their bags for Rouen, for Dijon, for Lourdes, for Marseille, for just down the street. Bitter, disappointed, humiliated, branded 'losers' before they had properly begun, these *children* had joined the long list of victims of a voyeuristic enterprise. David, Virginie and I, giddy with self-satisfaction, swept past the downcast second-raters with sincere nods of 'hard cheese', and made our way to the nearby Dôme for oysters and wine.

'That sound you hear,' I said to La Valoise, two days after the competition, 'is of doors opening before David, of barriers crashing down, of . . . '

Yes, yes, yes. Weren't we something, our little team? We patted ourselves on the back, with hindsight we assumed the inevitability of David's triumph, we took and bestowed credit in a frenzy of self-congratulation. With only the tiniest nod of thanks to Monsieur Chanat, we revelled in our patently fortunate victory. We thought, moreover, that we *deserved* it.

That was the night you drunkenly echoed Hobbes by announcing that life was 'pastis, brut and port'.

That was the night you serenaded Le Cocktail with your rendition of 'Moon River' in the style of Liszt.

That was the night you announced to all who would listen that you had personally 'made a star of David'.

That was the night David got publicly drunk for the first time; he showed every sign of being a genial inebriate, of the sort who expresses love for recent acquaintances and a general feeling of warmth for mankind. With watery eyes he looked from speaker to speaker, like a well-behaved dog, and sheepishly laughed off praise. He listened to your strained puns, to my rather soppy reminiscences of competitions gone by, to my various friends' musical triumphs and disasters. Virginie was there, and your younger brother (who told such entertaining anecdotes drawn from the world of civil-engineering), and several of my chess and music cronies.

The night was also memorable – although the event does not make its way into the runaway train of your narrative – because at midnight David asked for quiet and announced to one and all that he was in love. I called for more champagne and asked him to tell us *everything*.

'Her name, her name,' I demanded.

David wriggled, covered his eyes, folded up his body on the banquette.

'Her name!'

David looked up at us from beneath his thick hair. 'Geneviève,' he said.

There were sighs of appreciation all around the table.

'Beautiful!' I said. 'Geneviève!'

Geneviève was duly toasted, and I continued my interrogation.

'I gather the attraction is mutual?'

David was really writhing now. 'I think so.'

'She is a classmate of yours?'

'One year behind.'

'Adorable.'

David beamed and lit a cigarette.

'Have you met her outside of school?'

'Twice.'

'Twice! A torrid affair! What have you done?'

'We had coffee together. Twice.'

Everyone at the table was delighted. Even you.

'Have you played the piano for her?'

David was suddenly cross. 'I couldn't do that.'

'You can't play for Geneviève?'

'No.' David said this with conviction.

'Why on earth not? She will be swept off her feet. Any girl would be.'

David fidgeted and shook his head. 'Too embarrassing. I know what I want to do.'

'Now, David,' you said, fearing the worst.

'Go on David,' I said. 'What is it you want to do?'

'I want to get a motorbike. Just a little one.'

You were quickest off the mark: 'Ab-so-*lute*-ly not. It is *out* of the question. You will *not* have a motorbike. It is quite simply *out* of the *question*.'

Everyone at the table stared at you.

'No no, it is not worth discussing. A motorbike, *indeed*.'

'I think I should have one,' said David, reasonably, 'so that I can take Geneviève to the cinema.' And, inevitably, 'All the boys have motorbikes.'

'Now, I'm sure that isn't true,' you said.

'It is.'

'Even so, "all the boys" don't play the piano.'

'Some of them do.'

You chuckled at this. 'I think you understand my meaning, David. Have you asked your parents?'

'Yes.'

'And what did your parents say?' You folded your arms, as if the discussion were about to come to an end.

'They said to ask you and Pierre.' David thought quickly. 'Mostly to ask Pierre,' he added, looking at me hopefully.

'What a lot of responsibility,' I said, more than anything amused by how seriously you had taken David's perfectly natural wish. I could feel your disapproving eyes upon me.

'Look,' you said, to pre-empt any conciliatory remarks on my part, 'it is too dangerous, it is unnecessary, you must protect yourself, you will not have a motorbike, and that is *final*.'

David had a motorbike at ten the following morning, paid for by me as a reward for his scintillating performance of the *Death Spiral*, with his parents' resigned approval. I sat in a café and watched him drive it up and down the Avenue de la Grande Armée, his arms stiff on the handlebars, giddily smiling despite his efforts to appear nonchalant.

That evening I had the pleasure of meeting Geneviève for the first time. Full of excitement, David called me and told me to meet him on the terrace of the Père et Fils. I sat outside in the waning sunlight reading over the manuscript of my article on Chanat, into whose work I felt I had fresh insight. I said hello to friends, but did not allow them to join me. At last, David buzzed down the street on his motorbike, up on to the wide pavement, and lurched to a halt in front of the terrace. Sitting side-saddle on the mud-guard behind him was Geneviève. She hopped down and shook her long brown hair. It was the most charming scene: David trying his best to look purposeful and grown-up as he raised the bike on to its rest; Geneviève enchantingly pretty and seemingly years older than David; and then, as if they had rehearsed in advance for my benefit, holding hands conspicuously as they walked over to my table.

I said hello formally and tried not to smile. Geneviève ordered lemon squash and David insouciantly requested champagne. He was an artiste in love, after all.

'We've just been to see my parents,' he announced, as if he and Geneviève had decided to get engaged. 'And I've told Geneviève all about you, Pierre.'

Geneviève proved to be a quiet and proper little girl from Neuilly, hence David's insistence on the motorbike. She was only just learning to snarl like a true teenager, and often lapsed into a delightful smile. She seemed to know nothing of David's secret life as France's most promising young pianist, or at least not to comprehend it. I guessed by her appearance that she was mainly interested in clothes and kissing.

When she went to the ladies' I asked David about this, man to man. He clicked his tongue and rolled his eyes and tossed his head impatiently.

'Come on, David. You can tell me. Have you kissed her yet?'

'Not really, no,' he confessed sadly.

'You really ought to, you know,' I said.

'When?'

'Right now.'

'How?'

'Here's what you do. I go to the gents'. You put your hand on Geneviève's knee, like this, and give her a nice kiss on the cheek. Then keep your face next to hers. She'll kiss you, I promise.'

'You can't mean it.'

'David, I promise you. Don't you trust me? Get it right, though. Hand on her knee, nice kiss on the cheek with a smile, and keep your mouth available. She'll do the rest. Ah, here she comes.'

'Don't watch,' said David, who in his panic had begun to glare at me as if in a rage.

'Never,' I said. I stood and excused myself just as Geneviève regained our table.

Peering through the leaves of a potted plant near the bar inside the Père et Fils, I watched David pull himself together and prepare for committal. It took him a minute or so, but he was forced to act by the prospect of my return. How adorable it was, Geoffrey. He did just as I'd said, with some flair: hand on knee, nosing her hair out of the way, friendly kiss, nice smile. Geneviève did not disappoint. Girls are so wonderful in this way. She reached around the back of his neck with both hands, pulled his head to her, and kissed him with all the expertise of a film addict. A few of my friends from behind the bar had joined me to watch, and I only just managed to prevent them from whistling and applauding.

When the kiss ended, David rested his head on Geneviève's shoulder for a second or two, then sat up and reached for his champagne as if nothing had happened. I reappeared with so broad a smile on my face that David knew I had seen everything. He winked at me, a wink he had perfected since his piano début. After a few minutes' chat with Geneviève, I made my excuses and left them alone on the terrace, feeling very pleased with David and myself.

All in all, I must confess, I was not thrilled by David's new taste for independence, a tendency La Valoise encouraged to such an extent that David's parents and I were forced to intervene on numerous occasions. I have always striven to be non-judgemental, and I could easily understand at the time why David wished to celebrate both his Gaston-Robert victory and his

early Bac, but I tried to draw the line at cigarettes,
alcohol, fast cars and women.

Tobacco, the occasional glass of champagne, a glorified velocipede, and Geneviève, you mean.

I detected in David's behaviour a certain . . . demoralization — yes, that is the word — as if after his great initial successes he felt let down by the practical responsibilities of his art. He undoubtedly felt torn between my rather strict advice and that of La Valoise, who so eagerly pandered to David's more — shall we say — juvenile desires. David's parents, I am afraid to say, were often easily persuaded by La Valoise's arguments, if only because of his native French. I stated my case as clearly as I could, then returned to London in 1972 to take up an interesting conductor's post. I would not see David for eighteen months, and then I would not recognize the fresh-faced prodigy I had left behind.

Prodigy, shmodigy. What you really *hated*, of course, was the apparent effortlessness of David's balancing act between his personal and pianistic lives. You must have felt that to gain musical achievement something must be paid in return: you considered it a moral equation, rather than a simple allocation of time. Much as I hate to harp on this sore subject, Geoffrey, I have to repeat that your fifteen or so years of post-adolescent graft (and likely virginity) must have set you against those who seemed to make musical progress and enjoy the finer pleasures at the same time, including, heaven forbid, those of the flesh.

I am almost ashamed to write it down, but the fact of the matter is that La Valoise, whose incontinent love life no serious person could maintain for a week, much less a lifetime, practically steamrollered David into adult behaviour for which he was indubitably not prepared.

116

Indubitably? I can just see your twisted mouth as you say that word. You've always been such an old lady, Geoffrey. I wonder, if your educational institutions had not made such a situation virtually impossible, how you would have coped with an extraordinarily pretty and loving French girl who asked you with great warmth and sincerity to take her to bed for the first time. This happened to David. He said, 'Sure thing.'

Still, your choice of the word 'demoralization' is forgivable and correct enough. What budding virtuoso of his generation wouldn't be demoralized? I am just old enough to have been taught by students of the great composer/pianists. I shook the hand of Richard Strauss. But David Debrizzi belonged to the first crop of pianists to be born into a barren musical world, where the repertoire was truly stagnant and antique. David's disappointment, if he had time to feel any while his first girlfriend paid attention to him, was that for the rest of his life music would always mean the same names, the same notes, the same 'echo of distant thunder', to use the phrase you applied to Liszt. Imagine knowing that you were going to have to play Chanat's *Death Spiral* every few days for the rest of your life. David was precocious in more ways than one: he had already begun to roll his eyes sarcastically at most of the sentimental breast-beating that audiences around the world paid fortunes to hear. If my prejudices in any way turned David against the music that would make him a good living over the years, I would not be in the least surprised, nor remorseful. A large portion of our conversation was an attempt to demystify great music, to take it out and beat it like a carpet. I have no doubt that his playing profited from these sometimes amusing exercises, and anyway a good chat with David was worth a thousand arpeggios.

Your

CHAPTER SIX

I admit that I was at wits' end. Not only had La Valoise guided David towards the – I am afraid to say – demeaning sideline of a less-than-first-rate piano quartet, but plans were afoot for him to take David away on a prolonged stint of world travel!

Here you are, still railing. In my defence I must juxtapose David's situation with that of Igor Malechievich.

America had taken Igor to its bosom. Critics continued to employ the language of beatification. Dangerous, shifty-eyed cocaine addicts vied for the film rights to his life. Principal Records, bowing not for the first time to commercial imperative, filled the stores with Igor's first, hastily recorded album. The jacket showed Igor, thick-lipped, trying to look dignified and aloof on a tug-boat beneath the Statue of Liberty. Inside, good God, was the Moonlight Sonata, of all *recherché* works, and on to the vinyl were pressed for eternity half-a-dozen unmistakable clangers and a first movement of such saccharine character that third-rate amateurs everywhere must have rejoiced and said, 'You see? That *is* how it's played.'

Igor toured up and down the United States for a solid nine months. He was given the keys to so many cities and towns that he required an extra steamer trunk to transport them. His every interview began with such challenging questions as 'How does it feel to be free at last?', and 'Is it easier to express your genius in the best country in the world?' In his charmingly broken English, Igor maintained that, as a genius, he was perhaps more qualified than anyone to state categorically that the United States of America was very, very different from his homeland, and had all sorts of valid reasons for considering itself a superior place for concert pianists to work. Would he ever go back to the colourless communist concentration camp that was his homeland? 'Not for a million dollars,' he said, which, not coincidentally, was roughly the amount he earned that year.

I have learned since then that old Boris, who was beside himself with greedy pleasure, encountered a few expensive difficulties when he learned about what they call 'income tax'. Boris pronounced it 'talks'. 'What is dis "*talks*"?' Boris wanted to know. Igor had to work extra hard to pay it off. Like many defectors, Boris was often befuddled by his new surroundings, and felt threatened by the American version of 'freedom'. Longing for the relaxed respectability he had enjoyed back home, but unable for all time to return because of the scurrilous remarks he had made on American television, Boris quickly fell into ill health and could no longer cope with Igor's affairs.

Igor jetted off to Japan when a window opened in his already exhausting schedule. When asked why he had agreed to appear in an advertisement for tennis shoes, he replied that the *talks* situation in the US was oppressive, and his father's illness, in the absence of what Americans called 'health insurance', had rendered him flat broke.

David Debrizzi, meanwhile, sat in the sunshine at the Place du Trocadéro, playing the third Brahms piano quartet for free. With my help he had assembled a crackerjack ensemble of amateur string players, who called themselves 'Les Diables'. We used Henri's commercial van to transport a

119

Steinway belonging to a friend of mine who lived in the 16th and couldn't care less what we did with it; Virginie, as always, was on hand to perform the tuning chores. We had lunch-hour listeners in their hundreds, and thanks to the Japanese and American tourists David and his group must have been photographed ten thousand times in three afternoons. I was sorry not to see one of those pictures in your book. I doubt if David was ever happier. Little Geneviève, who often sat beside David during the performances, would have lent a little glamour to your stony-faced portrait pages.

Demeaning, you say. I suppose you like to think of yourself as a purist, and purists believe that a pianist's place is in the concert hall. Low human behaviour, such as smiling, is *verboten*. Clothes? Funereal. Posture? Rigid. Expression? Solemn. And to share one's music with a collection of bowing hacks? Never. Your top-flight pianist plays alone, or on occasion at the centre of a gigantic orchestra of his inferiors. Just like Igor, really. I suppose to say that David was having fun would be to miss the point of serious music.

You are quite correct when you write that for David's seventeenth birthday I took him on a lengthy trip abroad. In my family that is what one did with children on the verge of adulthood. One packed them up and one showed them the world, a wonderful excuse for seeing the world again oneself. As I was never going to have children, I relished the opportunity of guiding David around the globe as I would have with a son of my own. I saw no risk to his musicianship in taking him away from the piano for several months – quite the contrary. David had been playing many hours a day for more than twelve years. A long break was more likely to refresh his interest in the instrument than anything else. It never crossed my mind that David's technique would suffer in the slightest – or grow any rustier than a month or two of practice couldn't cure – but you appear to be obsessed by this possibility and once again accuse me of carelessness.

The fact that I was arrested – twice, in two different countries – plays right into your hands. You extrapolate from these unfortunate events that our voyage was one of uninterrupted iniquity, of drunkenness and fornication, of consorting with prostitutes and other low-lives, of utter corruption. I simply must contradict you, as my voice joins those of the maligned thousands in history in crying, 'But you weren't *there*!'

It was a nasty morning in September when we departed from the Gare de Lyon. Henri and Camille kissed us goodbye, along with Virginie, Geneviève and Chantal. I still have the map of the world I brought along, upon which David carefully marked our progress in red ink. We did most of our sleeping on trains, zig-zagging around Europe, taking care to visit sites of musical significance when the political landscape allowed. When we did spend more than a day in any city, we stayed in sensible inns where I was sometimes encouraged to cook.

My first and lesser arrest occurred only three weeks into our journey, in Istanbul, in a country known more for its appalling prisons, I am afraid, than anything else on offer. I do not know the Turkish legal phrase for 'disturbing the peace', but it would appear that some such clause pertains to the act of hanging by one's heels outside a third-floor window at three o'clock in the morning, working on one's yodelling. I assure you that David was safely asleep in his room at the time, and that the two women arrested with me were legally employed hairdressers. If I regret anything, it is not the hanging upside down, certainly not the yodelling, not even being caught wearing women's clothes; what I do regret is that I physically struck the man who came into our room to tell me to stop yodelling, mistaking him for an unmusical fellow guest rather than the police inspector in mufti that he turned out to be. I soon found him to be quite a jolly fellow who spoke some English, and he told me when I was safely behind bars that he had never been slapped before. Shot at, yes; thrust at with broken bottles, yes; left for dead in the boot of a ticking car-bomb, yes. But slapped across the cheek by a Frenchman in a frock? Never. He told me he hoped that it would never happen again, *inshallah*, and after paying him a small 'fine', I was a free man. I got back to the hotel before David awoke. He need never have heard the story, except that I thought it would be amusing to tell him.

My second arrest, I am the first to admit, was an altogether more serious matter. I assume that I am still *persona non grata* in Egypt. In my defence I have to stress the point that David was nowhere near the scene of my disgrace. He had gone off with a guide to spend two or three days up river, after I had used my truly severe dysentery as an excuse for not having to see the dreary ruins yet again. In my feverish and uncomfortable state, I continued to make the rounds of family friends, some of whom were highly placed government officials. Call it intuition, call it luck, call it large amounts of brandy, but in no time I had come to believe that the Egyptians were planning to attack Israel on Yom Kippur, then only two days away. While my personal loyalties lay with my Egyptian friends, my moral and political allegiances rested firmly in the Israeli camp. I saw it as my duty to reveal to Israel my suspicions about the cowardly Egyptian scheme.

However noble my intentions, I proved inept as a spy. Finding a working telephone that also happened to be adjacent to a toilet proved time-consuming. Even when I succeeded, not one of the people I called in Israel was at home. I decided to try the French embassy in Cairo. This should have been my first choice, for having already made several urgent-sounding calls to Tel Aviv politicians, and been overheard by a switchboard operator at the hotel made suspicious by my shouted attempts to make myself understood in Hebrew, I was arrested in mid-dial. Thus was an important war not averted, but I comfort myself with the thought that no one would have believed a delirious tourist even if I had got through.

I never truly realized the seriousness of my predicament, not even while sitting in that bare room on the outskirts of the city with nothing to look at outside but small platoons of soldiers that could easily have been firing squads in training. What possible evidence, I reasoned, could the authorities have against me? This question was answered when I spotted one of my loose-lipped Egyptian acquaintances being frog-marched through the gates of the military base with his head hung in the unmistakable posture of guilty defeat. His inevitable confession was certain to cause my denials some harm.

Uppermost in my thoughts, I am ashamed to say, was not the impending carnage and possible Third World War that I still believed likely, but the ways in which I might pull political strings to get myself out of Egypt once and for all. I will say this for the Egyptians, they were quite generous where cigarettes and telephone calls were concerned. Perhaps they expected me to incriminate myself, or lead them to my spymasters. In the few scrapes I have had with foreign governments, I have always found it most effective to get in contact with mightily wealthy expatriates, such as my father's friend Urthandville in Cairo, rather than embassy functionaries. Urthandville lived in Cairo because . . . well, you know very well why Urthandville lived in Cairo.

No amount of nationalization could dent Urthandville's inherited fortune, and his late-night peccadillos were not only tolerated, but in many cases facilitated. It took several hours to locate him by telephone, but only seconds to lie to him about my situation and David's. Messages were left for David at our hotel so that he would know that I had not abandoned him, and that he should pack our bags. The complex negotiations for my release were initiated at once, which must have been frustrating for Urthandville, because the highest placed officials he tried to convince or bribe were all preoccupied with the secretly impending war. My jailers, who I thought seemed disappointed not to have been given orders to shoot me on the spot, were forced to release me at noon on 5 October. David and I were rushed to the airport and put on the proverbial first plane out. By the time we landed in Johannesburg, war had broken out in the Middle East.

*

The character of our trip after that scary interlude could not be farther removed from your omnibus 'description of a '*shocking festival of globe-trotting debauchery*'. Despite the impression we sometimes gave in public, we behaved formally towards each other in private. We clambered aboard trains, buses, hire cars, rickshaws, jeeps, bicycles, and went soberly about the logistical execution of studious travel. My brief was to show David the world, not vice versa, and I like to think we both comported ourselves in a dignified, almost reverential manner.

Because there is so little of interest to see in Asia, we made fairly short work of India, Sri Lanka, Nepal, China, and so forth, and skipped Australia altogether. (Whatever you may have heard about our hurried departure from Bangkok, I assure you these are insidious, groundless rumours, nothing more.)

In Tokyo we could not resist seeing Igor Malechievich's farewell concert. He was about to attempt a triumphant return to America, orchestrated by the recovering Boris, and had fulfilled his multifarious contractual obligations in Japan. He performed the standard fare of Tchaikovsky and Grieg with a university orchestra before a mere clutch of fans in an acoustically faulty, airless auditorium, stalwartly employing his old gimmicks of gauntlet dropping and lid slamming. He had signed a long-term contract with Mishigo, and as far as I know was required by international law to play only their so-called pianos until the company finally went out of business just a few years ago. It was a sad spectacle, and reinforced my conviction that David had done the right thing by travelling instead of performing. David would never forget his trip around the world, while Igor would spend years *trying* to forget his.

David had taken in all the sights in an energetic but dispassionate way, and practised rudimentary communication in every language we encountered, especially Chinese, at which we both excelled. He had drawn his red lines on the world map (dotted and illustrated where air travel was involved), and by the time we reached the shores of North America the rest of the world looked like an anatomical diagram of veins and arteries.

In Los Angeles David announced that, while he was grateful to me beyond measure for all I had shown and taught him, he found that he missed Geneviève terribly; he wanted to cut short our voyage and return to Paris and young love. America, he argued, was a place he would see soon enough, in perhaps more depth than ideally desirable. I saw nothing wrong with his logic. I bundled him on to a plane, and took the opportunity to fly to New York on my own, the only worthwhile city on the continent, in order to fall in love myself.

This was easily done. The plumper, more fun-loving women I particularly admired were plentiful and not sought-after in the beauty-obsessed upper-reaches of that society. If David missed Geneviève for the usual teenage reasons, I missed the company of a woman who possessed a sophisti-cated enough palate to enjoy the food I cooked. I soon met a music scholar named Penny Chazare, found her to be between jobs, and took her back to Paris and my kitchen.

'I hope you're satisfied,' you said to me, not long after my re-turn. 'David hasn't played a note. I beg him to practise, but he won't listen. He drives around on his scooter without wearing a helmet. He stays out too late with the girl. I wouldn't be surprised if he ran away from home with her. My God, she's only *fifteen*. Aren't you afraid he's . . . breaking the law?'

'If you are referring to the age of consent, I do not believe that he is.'

'So you don't think he's really . . . her?' You wiggled your fingers in a vague way, unable to supply even a euphemistic verb.

'I don't see that that's any of your business.'

'Oh no?' You were angry now. 'Oh no? Just what, then, do you think my business is?'

'You seem to have a busy enough schedule. Some of the reviews reached us while we were abroad. Congratulations, by the way.'

125

'My *business*,' you spluttered, ignoring my compliment, 'is to ensure that David fulfills his potential. I will not see him distracted by your . . . your *mores*. Do you think he actually enjoyed your idiotic jaunt abroad? Why do you think he returned prematurely?'

'He told me he missed Geneviève.'

'Pah! He was only being polite – as always, I'll give him that. No, no. He told me some stories. I got the idea very quickly that he was . . . he was . . . '

'What was he?'

'David was *ashamed* of you.'

I tried to pretend this didn't wound me. You know how easily I am driven to tears.

'I rather doubt that,' I said.

'In any case I think this is the last straw. I intend to tell David's parents that I want him to find a new teacher. They must know by now that you are not strict enough with David, not committed enough. I won't let them continue this course out of sympathy or tact. I'm sorry, but that is what I am going to tell them. The decision will be theirs. I do hope you realize this is nothing personal. I admire you in so many ways, and . . . and so on. Only in David's best interest. But, if they do not take my advice and replace you, my own services will no longer be available to them.'

What could I say? I went home and cooked a splendid *coq au vin* for Penny, and trusted the Debrizzis to side with me. You always believed that Henri and Camille only let me continue for as long as I did because they were in awe of my social background, rather than for any positive effect I might have on their son. It is true that I was generous with my time, and sometimes, when I had it, with my money; but I doubt very seriously if they felt the slightest class pressure, a paranoia more often associated with your little country than mine. I honestly believed that they would call your bluff, and, if necessary, abandon you altogether.

What you said to them, then, I have no idea. You give no clue in your book. Whatever it was, it could hardly have been polite, or even remotely true, because they did not even inform me in person when they decided to enlist the services of Madame Helzenberg. David called me, confused, and asked me what had happened. As a matter of principle I had to tell him to obey his parents, much as it hurt me to do so. And I told him for God's sake to stop being such a coward and to practise, with Geneviève sitting on his lap if necessary.

I had known Madame Helzenberg all my life. I would have been the first to admit that she was a fine teacher, or had been until about thirty years previously, when she had lost her mind. At eighty-seven she was a shadow of her former self, I am sure you would agree.

> *In the mold of Wanda Landowska, Judith Helzenberg had run a glamorous piano-teaching salon in Paris since the Great War. It was my almost superstitious fantasy that David would be her last pupil, that he might catch on her dying breath a secret of music she had saved from generations of pianists and would only divulge to the very best . . . or the very last.*

What a dramatic and macabre idea. This would have been a good moment for you to add that one of the rumours surrounding Judith Helzenberg was that she was actually Franz Liszt's *daughter*. Don't you think a dying-breath transferal of Liszt's *daughter's* piano secrets might have been a good touch? But you don't deal in rumours. Not much, you don't.

I cannot pretend that your palace coup did not cause me distress. Even marrying Penny didn't quite cheer me up. I thought of taking on another student, but after David they all looked so bland, so hopeless. They couldn't play the *Death Spiral* if their lives depended on it. For a month or so I worked very little, tried to make Penny happy, spent some time with my fading father. I heard through my musical contacts that David had been seen dutifully entering the home of Judith Helzenberg twice a week, staying for an hour or more, then buzzing away on his faithful scooter with his music books lashed to the fender. This meant at least that he had begun to work again, because even in her deep senility Madame Helzenberg could recognize, and would never have tolerated, a pupil's sloth.

Then, late one night, as I helped Penny with the washing up, my doorbell sounded. I answered the door to find David, half concealed in the shadows, as if he were hiding from sinister pursuers. I ushered him through the door and upstairs to the main drawing room. I told him I was happy to see him, and gave him a glass of wine. I introduced him to Penny, whom he had never met, and told him that we were married. Then I asked him what was the matter.

'You don't know,' he said. 'You just have no idea how horrible it is with Madame Helzenberg.'

'She taught me, once,' I said. 'I have an inkling. She can be awfully tough.'

David lit a cigarette with the lighter I had given him, which had once belonged to a nineteenth-century descendant of one of the Couperins.

'*Tough*?' he said. 'She's out of her *mind*.'

'Now, David,' I said. 'She's terribly, terribly old. You have to be patient with her. I'm sure she has her lucid moments. You must try to take advantage of anything she still has to offer. She is a great lady.'

'She doesn't know who I am. I have to reintroduce myself every lesson. She falls asleep. It's very frustrating.'

'Does she still play?'

'That's the amazing thing. I will have sat there at the piano for half an hour while she sleeps in her chair, just sitting without doing anything, listening to her breathing, expecting her breathing to *stop*, in fact. Then suddenly she'll cough and wake up, and limp slowly over to me, push me aside, sit down at the piano, and play something.'

'What does she play?'

'That's the eeriest part. She plays Mozart concertos. Only Mozart concertos, and she sits silently through the orchestra parts. I've counted along, and she plays the rests perfectly. As if she's hearing the orchestra. And she plays *loudly*, Pierre,

128

with more power than you would think possible. She can hardly lift her coffee cup, but at the piano she has great force. I watch her hands, and they tremble awfully when she isn't playing. Even just over the keys, her fingers shake. But when she plays she doesn't miss a note. Well, every so often, in very quick passages, she will fluff something. But she keeps time as if the orchestra has gone on. That woman who takes care of her comes in to listen as if this were perfectly normal.'

'Isn't that interesting. Does she ever speak to you?'

'Hardly at all. Usually to ask me who I am and what I'm doing in her house.'

'Have you told this to Mr Flynch?'

'Are you kidding? Mr Flynch insists that she is one of the greatest teachers in history, and—'

'He's right, you know.'

'—and I don't want to offend him.'

'That's very good of you, David, but if you aren't getting anything out of your lessons with Madame Helzenberg, then you must tell Mr Flynch.'

'Her house smells like death.'

'Mr Flynch would say that is history you're smelling.'

'That old nurse who takes care of her gives me the creeps.'

'They've been together for as long as I've been alive. She's not a nurse, she's what's known as a companion. Do you know what I mean by that?'

'Yes.' David did seem to know.

'And did you know that Madame Helzenberg is said to be an illegitimate daughter of Liszt's?'

'You're kidding.'

'It's only a legend. No one has asked her outright.'

'That would be rude.'

'Yes, and it would spoil a good story. Liszt died in 1886. He was seventy-four. Judith would have been born just after his death, if you follow me.'

'So Liszt might even have died while . . . while *making* Madame Helzenberg?'

'Correct. It's only a story. But it's a good one, is it not?'
'Yes.'

'And it makes you appreciate Madame Helzenberg slightly more, doesn't it?'

'I already *appreciated* her, but I see what you mean. Still, it doesn't make her house smell any better. Anyway, not that I've been complaining to him, Mr Flynch keeps telling me how lucky I am just to be let in the door. It's kind of morbid, actually. He says I could be "her last pupil", as if I'm going to have to sit around there and watch her . . . die.'

'That isn't a pleasant thought.'

'No. But let me tell you why I really came here tonight.' David sat up on the edge of the armchair. Penny had left the room for more wine. He was a big boy now, his dark features set, his hair long and thick. His hands looked authoritative.

'Go ahead.'

'Pierre. I just thought, if you still have the time, that we could practise together. Without telling Mr Flynch. Just the way we used to play tricks on him when I was little. That way things would be like before, except that I would have to go sit in Madame Helzenberg's house and watch her sleep twice a week.'

I was so touched I didn't know what to say. I reached over and gave him a pat on one of his hands. Penny had come back into the room with the wine bottle, which gave me an excuse not to speak right away. I poured some wine, and gave a silent toast to our new arrangement. I am certain David could see how pleased I was.

'Welcome back,' I was finally able to say. 'We're going to have such fun.'

David raised his glass again. 'Chess?'

For six months David visited my house twice a week, after dinner. Because he no longer attended the lycée, and was able to play all day long if he wanted, this was the most intensive period of study in his life. You never knew about this, and chalked up his notable progress to his exposure to Madame Helzenberg.

Together David and I pored over music, often simply reading from the page in my study, away from the piano. We listened to noteworthy recordings selected from my collection. Penny brought us coffee and often listened with us, adding historical context and the occasional gossipy insight into a composer's private life. We flitted through eras and styles partly out of enthusiasm, and partly to avoid the overexposure to one school or another that can render any music ridiculous. For each visit I tried to plan a surprise of one kind or another: a particularly historic performance, such as a piano roll said to have been played by Brahms himself; an original autograph, such as Chanat's 'Sicilian Girl' (I could not afford the *Death Spiral* manuscript, blood stains and all, which is on display in the house where Chanat was born in Montpellier). Almost every session ended with a chess game, played in silence. We kept a record of our best games in one of David's *cahiers*. He hated losing, and almost never did.

I suppose our unspoken plan was to continue this way until Madame Helzenberg died, which is exactly how it turned out. She died not, as you had hoped, in David's presence, uttering a death-rattle key to the universe, but tucked into her four-poster bed with no one to hear her whispered secret. I wrote her obituary for *Le Monde*, including the rumour about Liszt, which helped greatly to perpetuate her mystique after death. Her funeral in Père Lachaise – at the Edith Piaf end, I'm afraid, not the Chopin end – was attended by a diverse, international crowd of keyboard artists. It was a shame you were not invited.

David and I hung back conspicuously from the throng. The others seemed to share your superstition that as Madame Helzenberg's 'last' student, David might have been privy to a revelation. To that extent, at any rate, you were quite right to think David could profit in a supernatural way from the grand old woman. From the day she died, David inherited a cachet that was worth every excruciating hour he had sat in Judith Helzenberg's musty salon.

*I am proud to say that during the six months he spent
with Madame Helzenberg, David progressed in leaps
and bounds. I feel that I was justified in thinking that
a month spent absorbing the great lady's knowledge
was worth a year of La Valoise's slap-dash technical
training. David emerged, at almost eighteen, saddened
by his teacher's death, but prepared in every way to
meet the challenges of the performing life. Imagine my
disappointment, then, when David came to me and
insisted that he return to a further course of study
with La Valoise.*

I think we can all imagine your disappointment by now,
Geoffrey. How you must have paced the galleries of Dollsworthy in frustration. To think! Your precious David back
in the clutches of the lunatic Frenchman, exposed to God
knows what kind of Continental depravity! You wanted
David to yourself, now that you considered him ready to
take the concert stage. You wanted to take him to London
and show him off to your friends.

In the end you had to agree to David's request, because
he simply insisted. He was old enough to make decisions
for himself. He had also developed a rare but awesome
temper. It was as if during all those years of calm, of
industry, of patience, an ire had welled up inside him that
now required occasional release. I saw it myself. His anger
usually manifested itself in the not-suffering-fools category
of sarcastic jibes; but sometimes, if something or someone
truly frustrated him, I saw the bare rage in his eyes, and
ducked. This anger never had a physical outlet, just the most
heart-piercing glares or remarks. I wouldn't be surprised if it
were one of those looks that changed your mind and made
you decide to allow David to 'return' to me.

You were famous now. Your conducting, although to some
it smacked of dilettantism given your other activities, was
greatly in demand. Shockingly, you remarked in an interview
two years later that *opera* had long been the love of your

132

life, and that you hoped soon to direct a work by, say, who knows, Verdi?

Opera? Why *opera*? I asked myself. You had never mentioned an interest in *opera*.

The answer, of course, was Mary Hatton, and for the first time in my life I actually envied you. I had met Mary on numerous occasions, since the day her father brought her to hear me play at Sindgewick Hall in 1958. I met her before my concert, in my dressing room. Monsieur Presteron had thought it wise that I make influential contacts in London, and had inflated ideas about Peter Hatton's power as a musical patron. Who cared, though, when Peter Hatton's daughter was so enchanting. My age exactly, but poised and mature; I was captivated.

Inexplicably, the attraction was not mutual. For fifteen years or more I never saw her except across crowded rooms at large social gatherings. When my London sources reported seeing the two of you together (and when I heard you had decided that *opera* was your true calling), I was struck by the inevitability of it all. Of *course* you would be the one to marry Mary.

I only wish I had been the one to introduce you to Mary – much as I would have hated seeing you carry her away – just to maintain my perfect record as your personal matchmaker. As it was I could only sit back and admire your success and good fortune. To be honest, I should add that I was happy for you. You were forty-three years old, had come into your own professionally, and on your arm clung the most desirable of reputable women.

I married Mary Hatton in June of 1976, a personal matter I must inject into the chronicle of David's life if only to illustrate again the appalling behaviour of his once and future role model, La Valoise.

Must you?

My wedding only just survived his attendance.

I remember.

Out of place in morning coat and top hat . . .

As opposed to politically correct pseudo-Bohemian high-fashion rags?

La Valoise arrived with his usual superfluity of uninvited women . . .

One was my wife, the other a house guest; there were only two.

. . . and proceeded to launch what looked every bit like a last-ditch romantic charge on my fiancée.

I was so happy to see her.

She was not happy to see him.

Now you tell me.

I do not exaggerate when I say that La Valoise physically chased Mary around the churchyard.

You exaggerate. We were trying to sneak a cigarette together.

Even David, who was normally entertained by La Valoise's antics, was not amused.

David was amused, trust me.

Only the intervention of three of my burlier ushers prevented a newsworthy incident.

I went peacefully.

But La Valoise saved his most atrocious behaviour for the reception.

Patently false. My worst behaviour I saved for another friend's wedding some years later. You will have read about that.

La Valoise was drunk on arrival.

I was giddy and disoriented owing to a mixture of champagne and the anti-seasickness medicine I had taken to survive our Channel crossing.

He embarrassed my guests with a 'truth or dare' game. He asked married couples of all ages prying questions about their bedroom lives.

I reel from the gentle wet slap of your wrath, Geoffrey.

He told risqué stories about our Parisian adventures that were not only out of place at a man's wedding reception, but entirely untrue . . .

Even the one about the American girl – what was her name? – with the skiing injuries, who—

. . . including one about an American girl in two plaster casts – a story that, thank God, was too preposterous to be credible. My guests laughed nervously, and I thought at first that La Valoise would dig his own grave of humiliation and fall face first into it.

But I wasn't finished, was I.

But La Valoise wasn't finished. He tumbled about the room in a manner that I assume resulted from the effects of fashionable narcotics . . .

135

Got the lawyers in on that one, did you? I most certainly was not under the influence of 'narcotics'. I was under the influence of something you were too busy worrying about me to experience, which is what we addicts call 'having a marvellous time'.

. . . in search of my cringing new wife.

I found her.

He found her, and announced in a loud, unmistakably accented voice that he loved her. This was acutely embarrassing not just because she had been married only for a matter of hours, but because La Valoise's unfortunate new wife stood within earshot.

Penny understood. She trusted me to announce my love only for the most perfect women, and Mary, you dog, was perfect. I remember wrestling with my knowledge of human relationships in an effort to discover how she could possibly have chosen you as a husband. I'm sure I decided that at thirty-four, in need of offspring, satisfied that men never rose above the level of childish beasts, she might as well marry the first hygienic one who had the wit to ask her.

What happened next I can scarcely believe . . .

On and on you go, flinging sand into the eyes of history. What angers me most is not the obvious twisting of facts, but the overall warping of reality. Your Chapter Six – covering David's quintet; our trip around the world; my marriage to Penny; your replacement of me by Madame Helzenberg; Madame Helzenberg's death; David's insistence that you allow him to continue studying with me; your marriage to Mary; my behaviour at your wedding reception – is a seamless character assassination of absolutely no value to anyone interested in David Debrizzi. You finish it off on a particularly devastating note, and with your selective

136

story-telling portray me as a wild and dangerous animal.

I could deny your accusations until my wrist cramped permanently, but the overall impression would remain: I was at your wedding; I may or may not have insulted a very important man, then slept with his wife. When I first read this section I could not believe my eyes as I pressed on through the catalogue of my roguishness, until at last I reached the carefully worded paragraph in which, if I am not very much mistaken, you imply that I murdered the very important man with whose wife I had supposedly slept.

Geoffrey. This cannot be right. I am alive, I know I am. I can hear my heart beating. When I laugh insanely people look at me. So if I am alive, and if you have been pondering these events all this time, why didn't you simply ask for my comments? As you can see I am not averse to letter-writing. I could have helped you *not* write, as you have done here on this page beneath my left index finger, that I '*tore the dress from the bosom*' of your niece, and '*spat at the feet of a peer*'. Would it make any difference if I told you that your niece, whose dress I most certainly did tear from her bosom, had *dared* me to do so? Would it make any difference if I told you that the peer's wife had *dared* me to spit at his feet? It was a drunken, wonderful party. I participated. I could have, yes, slept with a very important man's wife. It would not have been the first time. Your surgical removal of most facts simply leaves me hanging by my jacket from a railing, hanging there that freezing London morning outside the very important man's house in Belgravia, a murder suspect.

Only I know what it felt like to be hanging there. Only I know what presence of mind it took for me to say to the bobby, once I regained consciousness, 'I am hungover.' Only I know the sight of Eaton Square at freezing London dawn while being grilled by detectives about the murder of a very important man. Only I know the chill voice, 'Right, then, you're coming with us.'

And you leave me. Your Chapter Six abandons me as I am marched off to the police station, a murder suspect. Freezing, hungover, stiff, off I go, out of your chapter . . .

*

I am sorry I lost my temper. Your Chapter Six had that effect on me. I feel slightly better now that I've had a night's sleep. Also news has reached me that I will be allowed a visitor. My visitor will be able to take me away from here. You would like my visitor.

The other patients on my terrace – mountaineering injuries, alcoholics, aristocrat junkies, nervous breakdowns, heart attacks – all know that I am writing a letter to you. They urge me on.

Your

CHAPTER SEVEN

Speaking of murder suspects – but no, I can take my time. My visitor has not yet arrived. The weather remains fine. I am deeply tanned and only cough every twenty seconds or so. I have nothing but time, and a few sheets of paper left.

Your Chapter Seven, having left me safely in the clutches of the police, is a pastoral one. It reflects your idyllic first years of marriage to Mary Hatton, and all but ignores David Debrizzi's transition from newcomer to fêted recording artist. Your readers could be forgiven for believing that I spent your Chapter Seven in prison, whereas my incarceration lasted no longer than was allowed by statute when no real evidence existed against me – that is to say, long enough to intimidate and threaten me to the verge of confession.

It might have been a close thing had my murder victim not reappeared that same morning, alive, and resumed his activities as a very important man. This persuaded the police that they had jumped to conclusions. Like my Egyptian captors of a couple of years before, they seemed disappointed at having to set me free; their attitude was that I had been in the vicinity of a non-murder, behaving in a suspicious manner, so who was to say I hadn't not murdered before, or wasn't likely not to do so again?

As for the allegation of adultery, wittily reported by your Frog-baiting press, my denials were heard as clearly in Fleet Street as if I had whispered them from the far side of the moon. But I know what adultery is, and on that occasion I did not come close to committing it. The very important man's wife and I had a pleasant chat as Penny slept on the woman's bathroom floor; we idly wondered where all the blood had come from and where her husband had gone. The blood, as it transpired, came from the same nosebleed that had required the very important man's midnight visit to a casualty ward.

Being hung up outside I remember less clearly, but would swear it had something to do with the very important man's two large sons, just down from their institution of higher learning, who must have liked me very much to pull such a comradely stunt. Unhappily, they forgot about me. I was left at the mercy of the authorities. The boys took their mother off to the country; Penny awoke on the bathroom floor, left the house, and must have walked right past her hanging husband without noticing him. The police found an unlocked empty house, a pool of blood, and a suspect.

I never said I wished to lead a quiet life. It is one of the burdens of the gregarious that conservative people look to us for laughs, for titillation, for scandal. In the end they disapprove, of course, and exaggerate all that might be sordid. Thus was my chat with one of your wedding guests magnified to the scale of high-society adultery and murder, which is all London will remember of me. In the same way, you present me as David's nemesis. In David you had a hero, in me a scapegoat. The rest is typing.

Let us look at the twenty-one-year-old David Debrizzi, shall we? Let us look at him without recourse to those same cute-little-child-prodigy adjectives you continued to use until the end. He was now a grown man, nearly my height but the opposite build. His Corsican descent had not

140

let him down, adding a swarthy seriousness to his good looks, especially when he went a day or two without shaving. He let his black hair grow just long enough to wave once at the collar. His grin still originated in bashfulness, but set against his dark skin it could often be misinterpreted as rakish.

He and darling Geneviève had long since gone their separate ways. His fondness for girls was what I would call healthy, and what you would call morally corrupt. It was around this time that he told me, in all seriousness, that he aspired to become the best lover in the world. I don't doubt that there are quite a few women scattered around Europe and North America who would gladly have assured him he had succeeded in his ambition. He looked younger than his age, and acted older.

For two years he had lived in his own flat in Paris, equidistant between his parents' house and mine. His survival was funded from four sources: his father's contribution; yours; a derisory arts grant; and his occasional work as a translator for one of my family's international concerns. He established himself in our neighbourhood as a 'reclusive' figure – not in the literal sense, but in the sense that people mentioned 'sightings' of him, and he was talked about behind his back. He was still referred to as an *enfant prodige*, and I can vouch for the social mileage that can be got out of that pathetic misnomer.

Any physical description of David is secondary. Like it or not, David was a pianist. You can talk all you want about sex, about Freudian sources of motivation, about vainglorious art, about a lineage stretching through history from Couperin the Great to Debrizzi (via Madame Helzenberg), but what we had here was a young man who, through tremendously hard work, had managed to position himself on the brink of world-class musicianship.

You still wanted to push David on to the concert circuit. I believed he was too young. The men are separated from the boys at this crucial juncture, a process that takes more than musicianship into account: stamina, energy, political acumen, massive powers of memorization – all these, added to a willingness to live on room-service food, are prerequisite. What worried me most was my belief that, in a sense, the touring pianist ceases to *learn*. Like an artist who descends from his atelier to flog his work, and therefore ceases to paint, the pianist on the road displays his wares without refining them. And David still had much to learn.

When I suggested that David go into the recording studio, one would have thought from your reaction that I had advocated his singing in a transvestite rock band.

'What?' you cried. 'Some vanity press, samizdat, Beethoven basement-tapes to hand out to his girlfriends?'

'Nice touch, the pince-nez,' I said. 'Goes well with the bow ties.'

'Do you really think so? I . . . Now listen to me. This whole matter must be treated with the utmost delicacy. Everything has gone so well until now. Do you realize how lucky David has been? *One* concert. *One* competition. It's amazing anyone has heard of him at all. They will be expecting great things. There is a proper way to do this: a concert series, several cities, a good orchestra, maybe, with a sympathetic conductor' – you paused and blew on your fingertips – '*then* a reputable recording deal, preferably long-term, and back on the road to promote it. That is the way it is done, these days. It all leads to the Tchaikovsky Competition, of course, if the timing is right.'

'David will never enter, you know.'

'Nonsense. What do you mean he will never enter? It is his destiny. The Gaston-Robert didn't seem to bother him so much. And he was only fifteen, then. He is a strong boy.'

'He will not do it.'

'How can you be so sure?'

'It simply isn't one of his ambitions. We have talked a great deal about competitions. He is through with them. He thinks it is wasted practice time. He would have to give up six months per competition, a year for the Tchaikovsky. He wants to enter the field at the top, not grovel around memorizing pieces he hates but thinks will give him an edge in front of a jury. He doesn't want that.'

142

'*You* don't want that, you mean. You've *brainwashed* him!'

'You sound like Boris Malechievich now, Geoffrey.'

We were sitting and drinking on an aeroplane on our way back to Paris from that disastrous symposium in Munich. Remember? You lost your temper with the German who said '*What* English composers?' when you told him the title of your speech. I think you were quite right to bring up the war.

'Look here, Pierre,' you said, high over Europe in more ways than one. 'I've made no secret of my disapproval of your non-musical influences on David. I have not made too much of a fuss because I think, deep down, you are a good fellow, a sympathetic fellow, you see.' Do you remember saying that, Geoffrey? Do you remember what it was like to be friends? 'But I am starting to feel – forgive me, but I really must say this – I am starting to feel that you are projecting your own . . . your own *neuroses* where David's career is concerned. It is the opposite of overprotection, if you follow, or a different sort of overprotection. You didn't like competitions, therefore David will not compete. You didn't like performing live, therefore David will not perform live. I do not think that I am being too conservative when I try to chart out a conventional route for David's . . . exposure.'

'Say what you like. David will not do it. He loves the idea of recording first. It is out of the ordinary. He will start a cult following.'

'How do you mean?'

'He is going to record the Chanat.'

'Oh, no. Not the *Death Spiral*, surely?'

'That is the plan. Subject to your approval, of course, Geoffrey.'

'I cannot tell you how inappropriate I think the *Death Spiral* is. No one has heard of it, not outside the business. It is . . . '

'Ugly? Is that what it is?'

'I don't know. Gaudy, certainly. But the point is, Chanat is an obscure character. Impossible to get people's attention.

143

Selling a recording isn't like impressing a jury at a competition, you know.'

'Ah,' I said, 'but people *will* have heard of Chanat by the time David's recording comes out.'

'Oh?'

'Yes.' I brushed at my lapel with my knuckles. 'It seems my little article on the man has taken on a life of its own. I will be joining you in the ranks of musical biographers. Your own publishers, bless them, have been kind enough to comment favourably on my proposal.'

'You're not going to write it in English?'

'I wasn't able to raise anyone's interest in Paris. There was a bland biography written by one of his grandchildren that appeared in the Twenties. More than that, though, Chanat is considered something of a disappointment to the French. We claim Chopin as our own, of course. We have his corpse. But Chanat, no, he lived in the shadow of the heavyweights. I thought in England they might root for the underdog.'

'So we might record in London, at least? That's where all this supposed excitement will be.'

'Agreed.'

Very tidy, I thought. I would have my book on Chanat. David would have his recording. You would have the glory of introducing your protégé to London. You still did not seem convinced, and we might have argued more about the matter had our aeroplane not begun to plummet out of control towards Earth, somewhere over Luxembourg. The pilot regained control, apologized, and offered his passengers free doubles. The remainder of the flight we spent staring directly ahead of us, contemplating the void. Nowadays I do not wait for the plane to start crashing. I contemplate the void from the moment the engines are started.

I thought I did a good job writing Chanat's *Life*. You will not be surprised to hear that I identified with him and his disappointments. I was lucky to have unearthed a particularly poignant letter written by Chanat to his older brother, the jeweller, in which he describes paying a visit to Chopin's

144

Paris apartment. Chanat sat with the great man in the drawing room as, guess who, Franz bloody *Liszt* played the Etudes on Chopin's very own Pleyel. Chopin contributed a well-known line to a letter Liszt had been writing, in which he claimed to wish he could play his own works as well as Liszt. Whether that is sincere or not, at least Chopin had composed the music. Can you imagine what it was like for poor Chanat? His letter includes the exclamation, literally translated, 'Whore of shit!' He thought he might never play again.

Play again he did, though, and the world is one long, horrendously difficult, supremely ugly piano piece the richer for it. My dramatic recreation of Chanat's attempted suicide could have ranked among the great moments in musical literature – could have, that is, had your august publishers remembered my *name*, much less my book, when I delivered the manuscript. I was so embarrassed that I did not tell you how your publishers had let me down, though I know you would have been glad to put in a good word for me.

Your solicitors were a great help in preparing David's contract with Profundo Records (or Abysmal Blackguards, as we later called them). David, Virginie and I spent a week in London choosing a piano and having it moved to the record company's private studio in Holborn. The boys from Profundo, who had never recorded a solo pianist before, were awfully impressed with our intricate preparations, and with Virginie's salty tongue.

Profundo aspired to recording only élitist music, but on the afternoon we arrived they were clearing up the wreckage of their morning session with a more profitable pop group. A band known as the Mental Blocks had managed to record and mix one song before deciding they'd had enough and needed to destroy the studio for publicity purposes. This was par for the course in those bleak British days, I gather, and the boys from Profundo had planned ahead: the most enticingly destructible pieces of equipment in the studio were already damaged or obsolete, placed there as bait for vandalistic rockers.

145

One of the Mental Blocks was still there when we arrived, sitting in a considerable amount of broken glass and blood, smashing empties on his head, incoherently criticizing 'them' (by which I think he meant 'the fockin' bahstids'), and threatening every so often that as soon as he was able to stand he would 'trash the fockin' Steinway'. He struggled to his feet and walked like a wounded crab towards the piano. He ripped the canvas cover from the instrument like someone doing the tablecloth trick, and fell backwards with the cover landing on top of him. He fought for some time to free himself, like a missionary caught in a jungle mantrap, then went limp. David and I wrapped him up and carried him to the lobby of the studio. I had a little chat with him over coffee and found him to be quite a personable young man. He was a student at the London School of Economics, and, thanks to the Mental Blocks and his sound financial training, a millionaire.

You were tardy and missed all of this because Mary had given birth to her first child – and your second son – three months previously, poor little fellow, and you were not yet tired of looking at him.

While the piano was being rolled into position and retuned by Virginie, David asked the head engineer if he could listen to the song the Mental Blocks had just mixed. The engineer seemed embarrassed, but kindly complied. David sat in the control booth and listened to the five minutes of grinding and shouting, nodding his head both times the one chord change occurred. To my knowledge David had never been exposed to any rock music, much less the head-banging variety spawned by your dire society ten years ago. He asked to listen to the song again, louder. It was a love song with a violent title I can't remember, and contained a line from Shakespeare pertaining to doomed lovers' frustration and the desirability of murder and/or suicide.

'I *love* this,' said David, after his second listen. 'It's just exactly like . . . like . . . '

'Like Chanat?' I said.

'Exactly.'

I saw what he meant. The Mental Blocks' song was Chanat without the years of tiresome finger exercises and expensive music lessons.

'Let's hear it one last time,' said David, reaching for the headphones. 'Then I'll be ready.'

An hour later Virginie and I had tweaked the piano to our satisfaction, David had warmed up, and the rather perplexed engineers had agreed to my positioning of their acoustic shells and microphones. I sat with David while sound-checks were made, then retired to the control booth to smoke nervously and watch the proceedings. David smoked and drank coffee and played when the engineer asked, while further sound-checks were registered.

I had long been interested in the effect new recording technologies would have on approved musical tastes. Chanat's *Death Spiral*, for example, was too long for a single side of an LP or cassette tape. Chanat's *Death Spiral* contained no natural breaks – just the rarest of breath-catching let-ups. That was the reason – discounting pianists' fear of the piece, and the world's distaste for Chanat's music in general – that no one had ever recorded the *Death Spiral* before. Our decision was to record the entire piece as written, and simply fade out and back in again for the disc turn. We knew that someday quite soon other technologies would allow David's performance to be heard uninterrupted.

Other techniques of recording – especially digital ones, to which Profundo Records still had no access – allowed flagrant cheating. If we were satisfied with the spirit of a performance, but wanted to excise a fluffed note here, a pedal bang there, we could quite easily do so. It was also possible to insert later attempts at the most awesomely difficult passages if they were not executed perfectly the first time. You will not be surprised to learn that I had no ethical qualms about using whatever methods were available to produce a recording that would stand up to the most rigorous technical analysis.

In David's case none of this seemed necessary. The engineer

rolled the tapes, and gave David his cue. David stubbed out his cigarette, placed his ashtray and coffee mug on the floor, cracked his knuckles, and flung himself into the *Death Spiral* at full tilt. The engineer's jaw dropped. After a minute or so he slowly turned his head and looked at me, as if to ask, 'Is it *supposed* to sound like this?' He looked back at David, whose hands we could not see. David's head and hair bounced to the music, his shoulders shifted to the left or right according to which register Chanat had decided to pillage at that moment. On and on it went, in all its desperate glory: tortured quotes from Liszt and Chopin, sarcastic jibes at Haydn and Mozart, failed fugues intended to honour Bach – sometimes all of these motifs at once, blended horribly into a putrid musical stew.

My God, I loved that piece. Enjoying Chanat was like getting along with a relative everyone else in the family couldn't abide. I sat with a score on my lap, not because I didn't know the *Death Spiral* inside out, but because it looked so fabulous on the page, as if the printer had gummed up his type-forme with ink. I followed along as David played, through thickets of spread chords, waterfalls of chromatic runs, scaffoldings of leger lines. It was almost as glorious as Chanat's original, blood-spattered manuscript; all of his marginal imprecations had been retained (*'Vite, merde!'*).

After fifteen minutes, satisfied that his levels were either properly calibrated or utterly irrelevant, the engineer took off his headphones and crossed his legs. I offered him a cigarette and we smoked together as the music poured through the speakers. Behind the glass, in the gloom and beer-stench of the studio, David played on.

'I've never heard anything remotely like it,' said the engineer, whose name was Glenn Parson. He exhaled smoke and shook his head. 'All respect, of course, but I hope we don't have to do too many takes. This is French music, am I right?'

'French, yes,' I said. 'Glorious.'

'And everything he's played so far is . . . is *right*?'

'Perfect. There are some trickier parts near the end. Don't stop the tape, no matter what it sounds like. Monsieur Chanat, he had a bit of a struggle with his art, you see.'

'Sounds like he wanted to drive pianists mad.'

'Precisely. That is precisely what he wanted to do.'

'Blimey, listen to that,' said Glenn, squinting. 'Old Chanat must have gone through a mile of piano wire.'

'That he did, Glenn. Do you know that we're listening to a bit of history? No one has ever recorded this work before. No one.'

'I'm not at all surprised, actually,' said Glenn.

It was exactly at this moment, when David was careering off into the triple-octave leaps near the end of the *Death Spiral*, that you barged into the control booth.

'Hello all!' you said. 'All ready to go, are we?'

Glenn and I cringed and looked out into the studio to see if David had noticed. He had. He looked up at you, then quickly back down at the keys. He hadn't missed the slightest nuance, if nuance is a word one can use about Chanat's music. He pounded his way through the staggering climax of arpeggios, and through the famous blocks of pianissimo eleven-note chords where the nose must be applied to G above middle C. Then, yippity-tippity BOOM, David had finished.

You were still looking happily around the studio, poking at knobs and faders, making Glenn nervous.

'All ready to go, are we?' you asked again.

'In fact,' I said, 'and as you've just heard, we are done.'

'What?' you said, all surprise. You looked through the glass partition at David, who had crossed his legs on the piano bench and lit another cigarette. He waved five long and exhausted fingers at you. 'What? One go and he's done? Right, I'd better have a listen, then. Would you be so kind?'

'His name is Glenn. Glenn, this is Geoffrey Flynch.'

'A pleasure,' said Glenn, and at his touch of a lighted button a cabinet-sized tape machine on the other side of the control room whirred into rewind.

Through the intercom I asked David if he wanted to come back and listen. He shook his head vigorously. He started to play a Bach Invention while dangling his cigarette from his mouth. The piece sounded laughably simple compared with the Chanat, yet so infinitely *sensible*.

You took the score from me and followed along to David's recorded performance. You nodded here, scratched your balding head there, frowned and sighed.

'Stop it!' you shouted, after five or ten minutes. 'It won't do. Did you hear, right there, the bass trill? Could do with a little more oomph, don't you agree?'

Glenn and I, who had heard the whole performance, made our disbelief known to you.

'First of all,' I said, 'it is the best performance of Chanat ever recorded.'

Glenn giggled.

'Why is he laughing?'

'Because, Geoffrey, as you ought to know, it is the *only* performance ever recorded. And second, *naturally* the bass trill needs more oomph. Why do you think we have the studio booked every afternoon for ten days? We're going to put oomph into that trill if I have to charge in there and play it myself.'

'Well, yes, of course. I'll just listen to the rest, if that's all right. Note down my suggestions.'

'Fine.'

While you did that I went into the studio to have a chat with David. I told him what you had said about the trill. He took the criticism well, and added, 'At bar 745, the semi-quaver triplets? I butchered two of them.' He demonstrated on the piano. 'That's when we had our little . . . *interruption*.'

'We've got loads of time. I say play it straight through five times over the next two or three days, and if we still have any problems we'll have Glenn fetch his surgical kit.'

You came bounding out of the control room, waving the sheet-music in the air. 'David! David, my boy!' you said. 'It was magnificent! You really are superb!'

'Thanks,' said David, hunching his shoulders as you tried to hug him from a standing position. 'Thanks very much.'

'No no, I mean, David, you . . . were . . . *divine*!'

150

You might have been talking to an actress after a particularly rotten performance, inflating her ego before sacking her.

'Just a few things, here, I've jotted down in the margins. Care to take a look?'

'Not just now, no thank you, Geoffrey,' he said. He had recently begun calling you by your Christian name. 'Is there a shower in the building? I'd like to take a shower and start again.'

'Of course! Glenn! Draw the boy a bath!'

Glenn looked up from his controls behind the glass and squinted at you with the disdain of the dues-paying union member.

'I'll do it,' I said. 'There's a shower down the hall.'

While David showered and soaked his hands, you and I discussed the music. Your suggestions were, I admit, concise and appropriate. As someone who had long ago learned to play, if not perform, the *Death Spiral*, I was more interested in the technical side of David's performance. My view was that to get every note in the right place at the correct tempo was doing Chanat enough favours. Your criticisms had to do with the sense and shape of Chanat's rare lyrical passages.

'I don't think I ever appreciated this piece until now,' you said.

'Geoffrey, you've never *heard* the piece until now.'

'You have told me enough about it. I just never realized there was such *magnificence* behind all the busyness. Liszt never wrote anything this . . . this *Lisztian*. Did Liszt ever play it, do you know?'

'No one knows for certain. Not in public, anyway. By the time Chanat had written it – and died – Liszt had enough music of his own to play.'

'I see. But he could have played it in private.'

'He never mentioned it in correspondence.'

'Probably envious, the old brute.'

'Liszt, I assure you, was never envious of anyone. That was Chanat's speciality.'

'I find it amazing that the piece isn't better known. Why has no one recorded it until now? Is it really – I mean I can see perfectly well how difficult it is, but compared to Rachmaninov, the rest of them . . . '

'Trust me,' I said, employing a titbit of argot I had learned from Penny, 'it's a bitch.'

'I see, yes.' You took off your glasses and cleaned them. 'Listen, Pierre, how long do you think we'll be this evening? I have a do planned.'

'Ado?'

'Yes. My wife and a few friends would like to meet David, make him feel comfortable in London. He may find he has to move here, you know, if all goes well.'

'It is entirely up to him. If he feels like playing the whole piece again, we'd better let him. Ah, here he is now.'

David came back into the studio with a white towel around his neck. For half an hour we discussed your stylistic suggestions and my nit-picking technical concerns.

'Right,' said David, at last. 'Get away from my piano. Roll tape!' He had been listening to the Mental Blocks, after all.

I rushed into the control room. With a finger to your lips, you trotted off to see to party arrangements. David stubbed out his most recent cigarette. Glenn hid his brandy bottle and started the tape machine. David collected himself, head bowed, for a full five minutes. When he looked up again he gave us a nice, self-effacing shrug, then launched himself like a rocket into the version of the *Death Spiral* that occupies our shelves to this day.

That evening David was shocked to see where you lived in London. He had thought of you as a writer and sometime-conductor, and expected a more Bohemian existence than anything he could have imagined taking place on the five floors of your Mayfair house. I had told him about Dollsworthy, but even I hadn't known of your immense *pied-à-terre* in town.

Your guests had arrived earlier and were now congregated in the foyer to greet your French discovery. A welcoming cheer went up and glasses of champagne were raised even

152

before David had been relieved of his coat. After his long day in the studio David was mainly interested in food, but had to wade through an improvised receiving line before he was allowed to touch the shrimp and sausages. I stood back and marvelled at your confident introductions, at the splendid balance you had struck between the social élite and actual human beings, and at your wife.

Mary Hatton – I could never think of her as Mary Flynch – spent fifteen minutes helping you to ease David into the gathering, then sped to my side for a more sincere hello. Neither difficult childbirth nor marriage to you had altered Mary. She must have endured quite a drastic social reorientation by marrying you, but she had survived the transition intact.

'Come into the kitchen, Pierre,' she said, 'and give me a cigarette.' She pulled me down the hall by my sleeve. 'How can it be that I haven't seen you since our wedding?'

I lit our cigarettes and handed her one. The kitchen pounded with the din of caterers' activity.

'You look wonderful,' I said. 'I may have to go back out there and shout that I am in love with you.'

'Oh, thank you, Pierre. How is your wife?'

'She couldn't be better. She is helping me with my book on Chanat. Penny is a regular ferret, when it comes to research. She is busy now, but will join me here in London in a few days.'

'And now, this David Debrizzi. He has become so handsome. It doesn't seem fair, really, that he is a genius on top of that. Geoffrey said everything went fairly well this afternoon.'

'Fairly well? It was a triumph. I doubt if we'll have to go back in.'

'That isn't what Geoffrey said. He said David would have to knuckle down, nose to the grindstone, elbow-grease . . . ' Mary laughed her smoker's laugh. She plucked a stuffed pastry shell from a tray in transit to the drawing room. 'Won't you have one of these? Don't tell me you've become abstemious?'

'I'm eating less, as a matter of fact. I want to stay at this ideal weight. I'll have only one.'

153

'You really are quite huge, Pierre.'

'And middle-aged.'

'I feel as if I've just awakened from a dream and found myself fifteen years older. What have I been doing all this time?'

'You should never ask yourself such a question. Are you working?'

'Don't be silly. I think I've become a socialite. And I'm rather good at tax evasion. I've decided I hate opera and will leave my father to it. Music should not be inherited. Mine is a completely wasted life, don't tell the husband and child.'

I told Mary that in my opinion she was an excellent woman, despite being a socialite. She took this in a friendly spirit, as it was meant. She told me I had a piece of mushroom stuck to the corner of my mouth. I removed it and we rejoined the party.

'My dear!' you said to Mary, flushed with the glory of David's social début, and at the same time transparently angry that she had disappeared from the party even for a moment. 'And hello to you, Pierre. David is going to play for us all!'

I could see David behind you, surrounded by admirers, shaking his head at me and making a murderous straight line with his mouth.

'We'll see about that,' I said.

'Oh, it's all set. We've had to convince him, talk him into it. Everyone is dying to hear him. I think the Chanat is on in a few minutes.'

'But Geoffrey, really . . . '

'It's all set. Oh, there you are, Gladys, Duncan, Victor, Tom – we're going to have a concert! If everyone will just sort of move along into the . . . '

'*Geoffrey.*' I had you by the arm, just above your left elbow, in a grip made superhuman by practising Chanat.

'That hurts.'

'If you make him play, I'll make a scene.'

'Do relax, Pierre. Have a drink.'

I squeezed your arm harder, which surprised you, and repeated my threat to do something so un-English that it would take you years to live our friendship down. I had begun to feel an almost pleasurable rush of panic, as if I were the one who had been asked to play in front of your greedy, pink-faced guests, to perform amid their nervous coughing, to trust the *Death Spiral* to your limp-actioned Bechstein.

'Let go of my arm, Pierre.'

'I'm warning you,' I said.

'Don't you *dare* speak to me that way in my house.'

This exchange was delivered in whispers; we were both pretending to smile. I let go of your arm, but fixed you with a private look I hoped would fill you with terror.

'Right, then,' you said, loudly, with the sigh of someone refreshed by cold drink. 'If everyone will just sort of move along into the . . .'

Naturally, I threw a tantrum. I raised my voice to object. I called on David to defend himself. When you tried to push me backwards to the kitchen hall I lashed out with my right foot and kicked you hard in the – hang on, I'll just wheel myself indoors and ask a doctor the name – yes, I kicked you in the *malleolus*, which had you bouncing around on one foot, yelping in pain, but still, of course, trying to smile as if nothing untoward had happened in front of your guests. David and Mary interposed themselves between my tantrum and your injury.

'Pierre, for goodness sake,' said Mary.

'For goodness sake, Pierre,' said David.

You said something too. You called me a bastard. You ordered me to leave. You had ceased pretending that a scene wasn't being made. I kicked you in the other ankle. While your shrieks echoed overhead, I told David to flee, that I would cover his escape. 'Go, boy,' I said. 'Go!'

David didn't go. He put his hands in his pockets and stared at the floor until you stopped groaning. When all was quiet, David looked up again. 'Let's go in the other room,' he said. 'I'll play for a bit.'

You and I exchanged glares as Mary led David past your surprised friends into the piano room.

'I don't think,' you said, 'that you ought to hesitate in removing yourself from my home.' Your cheeks reddened like hot coals; something pulsed erratically in your neck. You made a mental note to write about this someday.

In London, during the stressful ten days I spent in the recording studio with David – his historic rendition of the obscure Death Spiral, *by the French composer Chanat, is an undisputed* tour de force *– La Valoise behaved so abominably that we feared for his mental health. He reacted violently to the perfectly innocent suggestion that David perform informally at a social gathering my wife and I had arranged. Quite apart from the physical injury he caused me, and the embarrassment my wife endured, David and I thought La Valoise might seriously have jeopardized our important 'coming out'. In the end, David could not have behaved more professionally. With La Valoise safely locked outside my house, the boy performed a riotously funny parody of Bach's First Prelude, which he played in the overpowering and hysterical style of Chanat.*

That *was* Chanat, you bloody fool. And I was not 'safely locked outside'. I am not surprised that you decided not to write about where I really was. I bribed your dentured servant, Hopkins, who kindly led me upstairs. I heard everything through a dumb-waiter, including your introductory remarks in which you apologized for 'one of David's French piano teachers' who had 'drunk an unnecessary amount'. You skilfully glossed over the real reason for my outburst. You implied that, as if we all didn't know it anyway, ha ha, French people could be right barbarous – oh, sorry, David.

You introduced David as if you had physically given birth to him. You described his playing in a way that would have made me vomit from nervous embarrassment, had I been in David's shoes.

'I once had the honour,' you said, 'of hearing Artur Rubinstein play in a setting very much like this one. As moving as that was, I have to say that you have in store for you a virtuosity and depth that may yet eclipse the Polish master's . . .'

I had my head in the dumb-waiter. I wanted to crawl down it and leap for your throat. I would have given anything to see David's face as you pronounced sentence after sentence of undeserved, unlucky praise that would be impossible for anyone to live up to.

Then I heard David play Chanat's 'parody', which the composer would have preferred to hear described as his 'homage', and I heard your guests' delighted laughter. David did not belie his mistaken reputation, forged all those years ago in the Salle Thierry, as a playful virtuoso, good at parties. It was an enraging experience to hear two of the people I loved most, David and Chanat, being laughed at for the very things they took most seriously.

I started making noises in the dumb-waiter. The acoustics were such that my muffled groans sounded harmless enough to me, but reached the ground floor and your guests like the howl of an angry ghost. Many of the wealthiest members of the group, who could afford the time to cultivate daft ideas about the supernatural, must have thought it was Chanat himself. Hopkins, your butler, knew exactly who it was. Such was his zeal in preventing my discovery that I could have been decapitated as he pulled me out of the dumb-waiter by my feet. I didn't want to risk damaging his career, so I left under my own power, out the back, into a sobering London mist, into an unsobering pub.

Needless to say I awoke the following morning, in my hotel, with a hangover of some consequence. I like to sleep straight through hangovers, all day long if necessary, but your early-morning telephone call caught me at the peak of nausea and self-loathing.

'Pierre,' you said, and I'll never forget your hateful tone. 'What have you done with David?'

I replied incoherently, in several languages. I had no idea where I was.

157

'Wake up, man,' you said. 'What have you done with David?'

'Sod off,' I probably said. 'Get out of here.'

'I'm not in your room, you pathetic . . . I am speaking to you on the *telephone*, Pierre, and David's gone missing.'

'Gone where?'

'Missing, Pierre. Get a grip on yourself, will you?'

I was beginning to surface. 'I haven't seen him since I left your house. I take it you've tried his room in the hotel?'

'Of course I have. He never returned last night. He left here shortly after – that is to say immediately after he played for everyone. He seemed upset. Not surprising, after your . . . '

'Yes, yes, right, I know. He left alone?'

'Alone, yes. You wouldn't have . . . you didn't . . . have you introduced him to anyone at all, to any girls, that sort of thing?'

'As you have probably noticed, David is perfectly capable of making his own introductions.'

'I'm going to call the police. We can't just have him roaming about with . . . '

'He doesn't *roam*, Geoffrey. He's never *roamed*. It's early. He may have decided to take a long walk.'

'I hope you're right.'

'Don't worry,' I said, and went back to sleep.

We had more cause to worry three days later, when David had still failed to reappear. You called the police. I called Henri and Camille in Paris, and somehow managed to ask them to tell me if they heard from David, without quite admitting that I didn't know where he was.

While the search went on, I went to the studio every day to help Glenn mix David's recording. David had shown no interest in the electronic chores related to his work, so I felt entitled to meddle in this area. Because Glenn was used to more obvious mixing tasks, such as censoring expletives from the Mental Blocks' shouted improvisations, he quickly grew bored with my perfectionism.

I sat for so many hours listening to the Chanat that I no longer saw David or David's fingers in my mind when I heard the music. I heard pure sound, pure expression, and soon knew every quirk of the beautiful piano we had selected. It was marvellous to know for certain that when the torrent of notes near the end arrived, it would be perfect. I fell in love with the idea of an ideal performance, not unfairly aided but at least *facilitated* by technology, and I applied myself fanatically to the task of fashioning an unimpeachable recording. David had played an inspired, practically flawless Chanat, and it was my duty to coax every ounce of technological refinement out of the equipment at hand.

Glenn didn't see the point. 'It sounds fine to me,' he said, almost from the beginning. I told him the point was that David had recorded the first *Death Spiral*, and it was our responsibility to see that it was the last. I also related a few sound maxims about doing things right if you are going to do them at all – which if Glenn had known me any better he would have appreciated I rarely applied to my personal life. Glenn threw up his hands and relinquished control of his board. He napped on a sofa in the corridor while I fiddled with equalization, reverb, levels.

At about midnight on the third day of David's disappearance, probably delirious from exhaustion, I did something you do not know about. I had scrutinized David's recording so carefully, at great volume, track by track, that I had detected virtually imperceptible mistakes hidden beneath Chanat's wall of sound. All but one of these would have been inaudible except to someone who analysed the tape as painstakingly as I. But there was one section where I thought David's minuscule error might just be heard by a particularly discerning listener. I tried to ignore the passage, but simply knowing that a lapse had occurred finally fixed it in my mind and made it stand out like a broken stained-glass window. The microphones had captured only a millisecond that was undesirable in a forty-five minute recording, but in my fanaticism I could not let it stand. I had to fix the note.

In David's absence, I felt I had no choice but to perform the note myself, and to weave it into David's performance.

I went out into the corridor and made sure that Glenn was unconscious – not that he would have objected in the slightest to my harmless tampering, which I had no intention of concealing from him. I found Glenn snoring happily in a residual cloud of marijuana smoke, but just to make sure that I was not interrupted, I took the keys from his jacket pocket and locked the two doors between his sofa and the studio.

The piano was still positioned and miked exactly as it had been for David's first session. Back in the booth, I reset the controls. I created four new tracks to record the relatively simple mid-register chromatic run that contained David's error. I was excited, focused, and pleased with myself for my thoroughness. My concentration had taken my mind completely off David and whatever trouble he might have got into. I danced about the booth making adjustments, rechecking the faders and knobs, even taking the time to clean up some of Glenn's rather slapdash wiring.

When everything was set, I rubbed my hands together for a minute or so, feeling very pianistic. I probably laughed audibly at the idea that this was to be my recording début. With a conductor-like gesture I pressed the master record button. I swept back my hair like the virtuoso I was, and strode out of the booth into the studio, and took my place at the piano. I put on the headphones, expecting to hear David's playing as it built up to the moment where I wished to contribute my cosmetic overdub.

I heard nothing but a distant hiss. Still calm, I traced the headphone cord to its jack. It was correctly plugged in. The fault, I still supposed, lay back in the control booth, where I must have neglected to tie in the headphones. Back to the booth I went, annoyed that my private musical spell had been broken. I went to the board with my right index finger poised to punch in the headphones. With my hand still raised, I stopped in my tracks. I had seen a sight that hit me like a hammer: a row of red lights, the master tape turning smoothly in the corner of the room – the last minutes of David's performance being erased from existence.

Do I have your attention now, Geoffrey?

I tried not to waste too much time trembling and weeping – no more than twenty minutes, I'm sure. I steeled myself to listen to the damage I had done, with the typical hope that I had imagined everything and the recording would prove, miraculously, to be intact. I rewound the tape, punched in the speakers, and listened to David's glorious performance from about the halfway point. I sat facing the glass partition, staring at the piano in the studio gloom, and almost began to believe nothing had gone wrong. I perspired heavily as the section of the piece arrived, roughly seven minutes from the end.

It happened at the conclusion of a melodic phrase – to the extent that Chanat ever wrote conventional melodic phrases. A natural moment of silence, an intake of breath, and then . . . nothing. I felt as if I had tripped over my shoelaces in an art museum and knocked a sculpture from its plinth – but worse, because magnetic tape cannot be restored once erased.

Or can it? If Glenn had made this mistake, he would have confessed or committed suicide. Either way, David would have been put through unimaginable disappointment and stress. I thought that if this had happened to me at David's age, I might never have trusted the hocus-pocus of the recording studio again.

When I had stopped trembling and could think clearly, I decided that I was uniquely placed to restore David's recording, and that if I succeeded I might save all of us a career-threatening crisis.

I went down the hall to the bathroom and soaked my hands in hot water for twenty minutes, collecting myself, centring my mind on the task at hand. I looked at myself in the mirror above the basin and saw the face of resolve. I dried my hands carefully and felt the great strength and flexibility of my fingers. I strode solemnly back to the control booth, rewound the tape to the same spot as before, checked that I hadn't made the same unbelievable mistake again, and pressed the record button.

I approached the piano as if I were playing in Carnegie Hall – head bowed, respectful, determined. I placed the headphones over my ears and heard the reassuring sounds of David's playing. I felt alert and confident, despite the shock of my horrible blunder, and despite knowing that several minutes of the most difficult piano music in existence lay before me. My only stroke of luck that night was that my entrance would be made smoother by Chanat's natural pause.

As in any performance, everything happened very quickly and without normal conscious thought. I suddenly found myself sitting in the silent studio, in a sweat, with nothing but the hiss of tape-noise in my ears, with only the vaguest memory of the great, thundering Chanat I had just played. I closed the piano lid. I took off the headphones. I trudged back into the control room, feeling depleted. I casually pressed rewind, and lit a cigarette. I located Glenn's secret supply of brandy and took a sip. I listened to the tape with all the faders up; the transition from David to me would have to be undetectable, or I had failed. When the moment arrived, I had to fetch the score to make sure I had remembered the spot correctly. It was perfect.

I know you will now be racing to your stereo to listen to the new compact-disc release, to see if you can tell where I began to play. You needn't bother. The recording is seamless. I mastered it myself that night, taking the precaution of recording a dummy original. Even Glenn never knew. I went out to where he was sleeping, replaced his keys in his jacket pocket, and walked into the London dawn with the incriminating tape under my coat. I threw the tape into a rubbish skip somewhere below Fleet Street.

It is no coincidence, you know, that my playing was indistinguishable from David's. It is time for me to say that I had taught him *everything* he knew, that his playing could not help but be cloned from my own. You can imagine that I was elated at the time, in a selfish way,

162

and that my walk home to the hotel was full of pride and satisfaction. In the hotel lift I congratulated my reflection. In my room I found a note from David, apologizing for his absence and saying he knew I would understand when I met Evelyn.

Your
CHAPTER EIGHT

I was blamed for Evelyn. It was said that Evelyn only pursued David because she had heard about me from her mother and was intrigued by the possibility of test-driving a newer, related model. I gladly accept 'blame' for any part my reputation may have played in David's brief affair with so sparkling a young lady.

When I found David's note I called his room and Evelyn answered. We met for breakfast, downstairs in our hotel restaurant. They told me they had seen Hadrian's Wall together, and that David had driven a car for the first time in his life. Evelyn was the daughter of a music-journalist friend of yours, and reported that her father had been impressed to the point of worship by David's private performance. Evelyn herself could not take her eyes off David. I could see that they had spent a delightful few days together, adding to the excitement of new love by escaping without notifying the authorities. Evelyn knew nothing at all about serious music except that its practitioners were 'artists' and its devotees, in her short experience, were rich. She very much hoped I wouldn't 'take David away'; I told her I wouldn't dream of it.

David and Evelyn held hands and made me feel old. She was a slender girl. She wore a black leather cap, from which feathers of brown hair escaped at the temples. She had a soft and eager face that reminded me of my first wife's. Her voice was gentle and pleasantly accented. Her rosy lips showed signs of recent use.

I hadn't slept since entering the studio the previous evening, and in my combined exhaustion and elation it was all I could do not to tell David what I had done with his precious recording. Do you know, I thought he would understand, and be happy for me? As it was, I let the moment pass, and never again considered confessing. I guarded my private joy and guilt at having altered David's Chanat, and expected to treasure the recording once it was released.

'Have you seen this?' David asked me, opening a newspaper on the table. 'Igor is in town.'

I read the short review of Igor's concert of the night before, which I had not heard about. It was the first review of Igor's playing I had read that mentioned neither his defection nor his having been a 'child prodigy'. The reviewer called Igor's playing 'insightful', 'personal', 'melodramatic', but 'sometimes lugubrious'.

'My God he works hard,' said David. 'It makes me think I ought to—'

'Come now, David. Patience, patience. Have you told Evelyn about the recording?'

'Sure.'

'I mastered it last night. Do you know what mastered means?'

'Yes.'

'Well, for Evelyn's benefit, it means the engineers and I mixed the recording and made a more-or-less permanent version for the record and the archives. It is an outstanding performance. I'm proud of you, David.'

'Thank you. But I still think Geoffrey has a point. Just look at Igor. He has played a thousand concerts by now, all over the world. You know what Geoffrey is suggesting, don't you? He wants to take me on tour, personally. He wants me to play a concerto, and he wants to conduct. A début here in London, to coincide with the release of the album.'

'Sound advice, in most cases,' I began. I was going to argue my side of the story, but David suddenly dropped his head to the tablecloth and partially covered his face. 'What is it?'

'Don't look,' he whispered. 'Don't turn around.'

'Is it Geoffrey? He'll be looking for us.'

'No,' said David. 'It's Igor Malechievich. God, is he spooky looking.'

'Don't hide, David. It isn't dignified. He probably doesn't know what you look like.'

David raised his head and his eyes followed Igor across the room behind me.

'He's sitting down. He looks about thirty years old. He's reading a pink newspaper.'

'That's the *Financial Times*.'

'Look, they're bringing him food,' said David. He was fascinated by his fellow pianist. 'Cranberry juice, just like the papers say. I wonder where all his minders are.' David turned abruptly away and started to light a cigarette. 'I think he's seen me,' he said, through clenched teeth. 'I think he may have recognized me.'

'How could he? Your picture has never been in the papers. You've changed a lot in ten years.'

'You remember Igor,' said David, making a zombie face and sound-effects of the paranormal. 'He can *feel* me.'

Evelyn suddenly perked up. 'Don't look now,' she said, rolling her eyes. 'It's Geoffrey Flynch.'

David gave a worried look in Igor's direction, then tried to hide his face. 'He'll make a scene,' he said.

'Just relax,' I said. 'Everything will be fine.'

'David!' you shouted. '*There* you are!' You came across the restaurant so noisily that you might have been a wedding Bentley dragging empty tins. 'David! We were so *worried* about you!'

David was pleading with you and keeping one hand to his face to ward off Igor's evil eye.

'Where have you *been*?'

You were at our table now. It was evident from the way

166

you looked at me and Evelyn that you had decided the two of us must have conspired to keep David underground. You pulled back the fourth chair and sat down.

David began to explain, rapidly, where he and Evelyn had been. You listened for a second or two, your eyes wandering impatiently around the room, then raised your eyebrows and interrupted. 'Look!' you practically screamed. 'Look who it *is*!'

David all but crawled under the table. Evelyn, who knew nothing about Igor but had solid instincts, covered her face. I sat back and sighed.

'Here we go,' David moaned. 'Inevitable.'

'It's *Igor*!' you said. 'Look, look! It's *Igor Malechievich*!'

I tried to kick your . . . yes, your *malleolus*, under the table.

'We know who it is, Geoffrey,' I said. 'David would rather not say hello to him just now.'

You waved at Igor and bowed your head solemnly, like a rival knight.

'What do we do now?' I asked. I spoke out of the non-Igor side of my mouth, like a ventriloquist.

'I'll go have a word with him,' you said, pushing back from the table.

'No no no!'

'I'll just see if he wants to join us.'

'I'm getting out of here,' said David.

It was too late. We had to pretend to enjoy our little reunion as you spoke to Igor and motioned towards our table; David and Evelyn and I smiled and waved at Igor. I do believe he returned a scowl. You were so persistent that eventually Igor downed his remaining cranberry juice and came over to our side of the restaurant. At first he didn't say a word. He stood at the edge of our table listening to our muttered, nervous greetings as if we were groupies asking for autographs.

Igor was a big lad now, despite the famous diet. He looked weary and sad. His broad, pasty face looked as forlorn and distant – yet tinged with anger – as did the photographs on his two Principal record albums. He still

167

wore his trademark white scarf over his shoulders, and a white handkerchief tucked into his blazer. (If I know the superstitious Malechievich mind, it was the same handkerchief he had defiantly thrown down on the stage at the Salle Thierry.) His hands had the unmistakable pianist's look that has nothing to do with size or delicacy: they hung at his sides from slumped shoulders and dangling arms, but seemed to possess dangerous potential, like cocked pistols. I thought of the miles of ivory those hands had travelled in public over the years, and felt a surge of pity for Igor and all that he had endured.

You refused to let Igor go. You marvelled at the wild coincidence that two young men who were both pianists should actually be staying at the same hotel. You suggested that we lived in a microscopically small world. (I looked over my shoulder and recognized almost everyone in the restaurant.) You congratulated Igor on his reviews and vowed that we, as a group, would not rest until we had attended one of his London concerts.

I looked over at David and saw that he was mortified. He must have felt deflated by Igor's presence – the reviews, the breakfast alone the morning after a concert, the white handkerchief, your fawning attention. He must have felt like a child. He hid his hands beneath the table and looked ill.

'David here,' you announced – and you were able to do so because even I considered it impolitic to stuff a napkin into your mouth, 'is in London recording for the first time. Isn't that exciting? He has recorded the—'

'So Igor,' I interrupted, not wishing you to give away the Chanat. Igor had probably inherited his father's mercenary instincts, and I would not have put it past him to race into the studio and beat David to the punch. 'So Igor,' I said, 'I trust your father is in good health?' This was not a risky question, as I had read that Boris had survived another hospital stay, and seemed finally to have come to grips with Western income tax.

'He is feeling much better, thank you,' Igor said, in French. They were his first words to us. 'He hopes to come to London before my stay is finished.'

168

'How nice.' I remembered the last time I had seen Boris, and made a mental note to change hotels.

'Now Igor,' you said, hastily, 'we simply *must* arrange for you to hear David's recording. Would you like that? I think you would be terribly interested in the—'

'*Geoffrey*,' I said, imbuing my tone with the same finger-squeeze with which I had nearly crippled your non-conducting arm a few nights before. 'Poor Igor must be *terribly* busy. Think of the schedule, of the . . . '

'Actually,' said Igor, addressing David, 'I would be honoured.'

'Wonderful!' you exclaimed, and gave me a scalding look. 'It's all set then. Perhaps after your concert? We'll all be there, of course. We can all go back to my house afterwards and listen to David's tape.'

'I will arrange for tickets to be waiting for you,' said Igor, bowing in a military way. 'But now I must be going.' He made further excuses and departed, flinging his white scarf around his neck and over his back.

'I have never,' said David, 'been so embarrassed in all my life.'

'Don't be silly, David,' you said, pouring coffee, being avuncular. 'Now tell me, just where have you *been* for the last three days?'

I knew David had arrived when Igor Malechievich especially invited him to his recital in London. Igor must have got wind of David's long-awaited recording of the Death Spiral, *and wished to form an alliance with the young man with whom he expected to vie for the attention of the musical world.*

Wouldn't it be nice to think so, Geoffrey? This is the point in your book where I began seriously to wonder what your game was. All or most of your other errors I had chalked up to incompetence, semi-conscious self-glorification, Pierre-bashing. Now I wasn't so sure. I saw no reason why you should distort the simple fact that we bumped into Igor,

169

and you elicited an invitation to his concert, unless it was deliberately to overstate for your readers David's then practically non-existent reputation. Your motives became clearer to me from this point on, as your narrative veered from the improbable to the fabulous.

These were permissive times, and Evelyn was allowed to stay with David in our hotel. I did not see much of them. David showed little interest in hearing his recording before Igor did ('If you say it is finished, what can I do?'). The day of our breakfast, and the next two, he dutifully trudged off to a rehearsal studio I had booked where he was able to put in hours of useful practice.

I spent those days nursing my guilt, and convincing you to invite me along to your house after Igor's concert. I promised to behave. I apologized like a man for having created a disturbance the last time. When finally you told me I would be welcome, I started to visualize the moment when my playing would take over from David's, highly amplified, in front of two young men with superhuman ears. I hoped my own ears hadn't lied, that the transition was as smooth as I had thought, and that my own playing would deceive even the original performer. I was on edge, as you can imagine, and was grateful for the distraction of a few chess cronies I was able to look up and flay alive at the board. I called Glenn at Profundo's recording studio and arranged to have a cassette-tape sent to your house. Penny arrived in London on the morning of Igor's concert, which further took my mind off the touchy matter of my musical imposture.

Penny and I were nearing the date we had set for a friendly separation. She wanted to go back to America and take up a teaching post; I didn't want to go with her. My first two marriages both ended this way, with a divorce date set much the way a conventional couple will become engaged to be married. I remember your asking me why I bothered getting married in the first place, and my replying that it seemed to make me and my wives temporarily happy, and that we did not need a better reason. I have a flawless record of entirely amicable marriages, which is more than you can say. I have since visited Penny and her new husband in Westchester County. She has children, you won't be surprised to hear, and crushing debts. If I were to be entirely honest I would have to admit that you are more or less correct when you write that Gabrielle and Penny both left me because they wanted children. Heavenly cooking goes only so far, and it is a rare young woman who is any good at all at chess.

On the night of Igor's concert, we met at my hotel for a drink before taking taxis to Sindgewick Hall. David and Evelyn were so wrapped up in their love affair that they seemed to resent your constant reminders that we were to behave, that this was an important, 'career-shaping' event in David's life. Mary tried to calm you down. Penny told us of the discoveries she had made back in Paris pertaining to Chanat's rumoured syphilis. I smoked heavily and resisted saying, one by one, things that I thought might cause you to rethink your decision to let me hear David's recording at your house later in the evening.

Penny and I shared a taxi with Mary, while you accompanied David and Evelyn. Mary was unabashedly frustrated with her life, and made our driver go well out of his way so that she had more time to complain and smoke my cigarettes. We arrived at the hall with ten minutes to spare. An envelope was handed to me – to *me*, in *my* name – which contained our tickets and a note from Igor. 'Please,' the note read, 'will you keep Charlotte company? She is my good friend. She will be at the bar. She has blond hair and will wear white.'

Igor's 'good friend' Charlotte was visible to me from the foyer. She was striking, in a vulgar way. She was posed at the bar, I have to say, like a prostitute in a businessman's hotel. I worked through the impressive crowd, past posters of deadly-serious Igors, and introduced myself. Charlotte was American, and she chewed gum. I introduced her to our group, and showed her Igor's note. She looked as if

171

she wouldn't have blinked an eye had I told her we were all off to Heathrow for a flight to Bahrain, where she would be sold into a harem. I asked her directly if she was Igor's girlfriend, and she said she thought so, yes. I remembered the beauteous Tanya of Igor's adolescent years, and thought the young pianist had taken a step down in the free world.

We took our seats in the middle of the hall, in my opinion not nearly fortified enough to withstand a typical Malechievich performance. David sat next to me, excited by the ambience of a full and expectant auditorium. Igor's wretched Mishigo, black with white legs, gleamed on the stage. Just as the lights dimmed and the compère emerged from the wings to make his introductions, David jabbed me in the ribs. 'There,' he said, pointing a finger with his hand below the seat in front of us. 'First row. Do you see him? I think it's Boris.'

It was Boris, all right, his huge silvery head stock still, like the conning tower of a submarine.

'I suppose that means he will be joining us tonight?' David asked.

'No doubt, yes. Never mind. I don't hold a grudge.'

Igor took the stage, bowed once, hurled down his handkerchief, slammed open the piano, and we were off into the wonderful world of Ravel, à la Malechievich. I stole a glance at David, who knew the piece well, and saw him working his fingers on his knees, wincing now and then in disagreement with Igor's heroic interpretation. This was French music, after all, loathsome in many respects as it might be; David and I thought we owned certain rights to its translation.

Igor's performance was full of conviction and professionalism. I liked his carriage, his control, his command over the audience. I thought David would probably be quite impressed as well. I knew he could pull off a worthy rendition of almost any piece, but to do so night after jet-lagged night, the way Igor did, was another matter entirely. It struck me then that this was the reason you had gone to such embarrassing lengths to have us personally invited to Igor's concert. You wanted to

172

make David jealous. My conspiracy theory ran all the way to the hotel bookings, which you had arranged: had you known we would run into Igor?

I pondered this worrying question while Igor dashed through a sterling Schubert impromptu or three, then surprised us all with a Haydn sonata that he somehow managed to make slightly less trite than the written notes themselves suggested. Stout Igor sweated, strained, looked as if he could have used the handkerchief he had cast aside. His bravura endings were greeted with the kind of appreciative but restrained applause that says, 'Very good; but I want to be *amazed*.' The pauses between the movements, as always and everywhere, were filled with hideous retching and coughing, as if only consumptives attended concerts. From what I could make out in the concert-hall gloom, Boris never moved a muscle; I could only imagine what his eyes were doing.

Igor eschewed intervals. We were huddled at the stage door before we knew it, Charlotte wrapped in her mink stole, Evelyn hugging David for warmth, you remarking on the disgraceful human litter that were your fellow Londoners. Mary, Penny and I stood to one side, giving tourists directions. We were cold and impatient. David, over Evelyn's shoulder, gave me an anxious look. His part of the evening had not yet begun.

When Igor finally emerged, with Boris filling the doorway behind him, he apologized for having taken so long 'with reporters'. We congratulated him on his performance. Boris wanted at first to know who we were, then recognized me and beamed. 'We meet again!' he said, in Russian, stretching out his gigantic hands. I flinched, but Boris intended only an embrace.

We were able to walk to your house. I stayed back with the women. You and Boris strolled side by side in silence. David and Igor took the lead, hands in pockets, heads bowed, getting acquainted. I am sure you thought everything was going swimmingly.

The streets gradually narrowed and quieted as we neared your opulent nook of London. Hopkins showed us in, raised his nose and sniffed when he recognized me, disembarrassed us of wraps, gloves, and most outer garments except Igor's white scarf, which the young Russian defector clung to like a lifeline. You led us into the drawing room, where drink and cranberry juice had been laid on and the chairs had been formally arranged for listening to music. The dormant piano, under its black cover, had been consigned to a distant corner of the room.

You played master of ceremonies, trying to introduce David and Chanat's *Death Spiral*; the rest of us, except Igor, battled each other for drink. To break the ice, you told the story of Chanat's first meeting with Liszt – the symbolic value of which must not have been lost on Boris and Igor Malechievich. This story had been provided for you by Penny, but we hadn't known you would use it to tempt fate. In any case you got the story completely wrong, and left your audience with the impression that Chanat had tried to *kill* Liszt. What is it with you and your musical murders? First Sand and Chopin, then Chanat and Liszt – when will the bloodshed stop? Next will we learn that the sentry who shot Webern was an envious fellow-serialist? For your information, and because my biography of Chanat remains unpublished, Chanat *said* he wanted to kill Liszt, but meant it purely in the spirit of musical competition, much the way jazz musicians say they will try to 'cut' one another. That Liszt dashed off a panicked diary entry to the effect that a 'madman' had burst in and threatened his life, only serves to document the hubris of a man who could not conceive of anyone's actually hoping to outdo him at the piano.

Thanks to your little talk, Igor and Boris looked as if they thought they had been lured into your house in order to be slaughtered. The situation was saved when David, showing great poise, took the floor and thanked Igor for coming, and expressed his hope that Igor would enjoy David's humble rendering of the *Death Spiral*. He handed over my own well-thumbed score so that Igor might follow along with the recording. He sat down again, modestly, and gestured for you to roll the tape. The rest of us had, for various reasons, hit the drink in a rather serious way. We crumpled into our seats and awaited the music.

I was seated at the back, near the piano, so that I was able to twitch with nervousness without being noticed. I couldn't decide whether I should explode in a coughing fit when the moment came for my playing to take over from David's. I simply didn't think I could bear the humiliation if you or David – or Igor, for that matter – noticed what I had done. I looked about for props that I might crash into at the crucial measure of music.

The *Death Spiral* began. That certainly opened everyone's eyes, especially Igor's. He may have hoped until that moment that the rumours he had heard about this Debrizzi fellow were unfounded, or relayed to him by his father to spur him on to more frenzied practice. Here was final proof, from the very first bars, that David was a player to be reckoned with.

David was the picture of calm. I have seen pianists pretend to go into trances when listening to their own work. I have seen them conduct along. I have heard them sing and moan. I have seen them blanch, cover their faces, run from the room; smile, laugh, pound their fists in triumph; tremble, whimper, burst into tears. David sat quietly, listened along with the rest of us, exhibiting only the most natural expression for a musician under the circumstances, which is curiosity.

You, on the other hand, refused to sit down, gasped at the most titanic passages, slapped yourself noisily on the forehead to convey to us that you had never heard pianism remotely like this. 'Oooh,' you said. 'Aaah.' You did practically all of the things I have seen histrionic musicians do, except weep, which I assumed you were saving for the end. You conducted in the air with your eyes closed during the brief interlude where Chanat reined in the virtuosity and allowed us, for once, a clean line of melody.

Boris was thunderstruck. Igor slumped in his chair. Charlotte made smacking noises with her chewing gum – most of which, thank God, were inaudible beneath the music – and looked around at your antiques. Evelyn smiled at David, who couldn't see her from where he was sitting. Mary folded her

175

arms and tried to concentrate, then attracted my attention to get me to toss her a cigarette. Penny squeezed my arm and mouthed the word 'Wow'.

I found that I had emptied my glass, and that the drinks trolley was tantalizingly near at hand. I didn't know of any rules that said a man could not top up his drink during a taped performance, so I quietly stood and sidled over to the trolley. Five faces turned to me – yours, Mary's, Charlotte's, Boris's, Penny's. Four of those faces read 'Me too'. Yours was pure annoyance. Igor and David continued to concentrate on the music while I tended bar. For half an hour, as my moment of truth neared, we pretty well cleared the drinks trolley.

The transition point neared. I sat down again next to Penny, feeling very drunk indeed. She looked at me with a strange, worried expression, then took a handkerchief out of her purse and swabbed my sweaty brow. I decided to bear the terrible moment without creating a diversion. I clenched my hands together and stared at the floor. I could no longer look at David's innocent face. I felt as I had done as a teenager, on stage, listening to the orchestra buildup, waiting for my first entrance. I used to think I would faint at the inevitability of it all. Once the baton descends, there is no turning back. I used to sit at the piano the same way, hands clenched, staring at my feet on the pedals beneath the keyboard, praying for fire, for earthquake, for the concert master to become violently ill.

The moment came and went. I continued to stare at the floor. I must say that despite my powerful anxiety, it occurred to me that my own playing was superb – better, if I may say so, than David's version, without standing out as fraudulent. I did notice that you had stopped contributing your running commentary of ooohs and aaahs. This worried me. I didn't dare look up, for fear of seeing a room full of accusing faces. I waited out the climax, listened with a mixture of pride and horror to my stupendous finale, then took a deep breath and raised my head.

176

Igor was the first to applaud. Boris leapt to his feet and clapped his way across the room to congratulate David with a bear hug. Igor rose next. Shaking his head in wonder, he walked over to David and shook his hand, then leaned down, grasped David's head behind the ears, and kissed him theatrically on the forehead. Charlotte looked confused, as if she hadn't figured out that it was not Igor's but David's performance. You capered about the room, blowing kisses in the air, holding your hands wide and raising your ecstatic face to the ceiling. 'My God, my God, my God!' you kept repeating, in a kind of beatific stage-whisper. I took this as a compliment.

While you made a fool of yourself – not that anybody noticed in the general excitement – I took a hard look at David. His expression was enigmatic, to say the least. He might have been naturally shy, even insecure, but he knew acclaim when he saw it. It wouldn't have occurred to you or me to be in any way awed by Igor Malechievich, but just try to imagine how David felt. Here was Igor, a fairly renowned touring pianist with two good recordings under his belt at the unheard-of age of twenty-two, who was talked about, reviewed, well-off despite his father's financial naiveté, and who had jumped up to plant a Slavic kiss on the head of, let's face it, an unknown. David was justifiably proud of himself, and it showed.

What also showed, although at the time I was able to convince myself that I was imagining things, was a little furrow in David's brow, a thin line denoting suspicion. No, I knew I was imagining it; David was simply choked with happiness.

'And lest we forget,' you said, 'let's hear it for the producer!'

All glasses were raised in my direction. Igor, showing sympathetic manners I don't think we knew he possessed, came over to tell me what a good job I had done. He asked me well-informed questions about microphone positions and studio dimensions, while the rest of you caroused on David's side of the room. He also told me, pianist to pianist, that I had made the right choice with the Chanat. He told me he had never been able to find a score of the *Death Spiral*, so I offered to copy mine and give it to him if he promised not make a recording of it.

'After this,' Igor said winningly, 'I wouldn't dare.'

'Won't you have a drink, Igor?' I asked. 'Don't you ever get sick of cranberry juice?'

'Now and again,' he said, 'I pour a little vodka in. For nostalgic reasons.'

'Hopkins!' I cried. 'Vodka, man, vodka!'

There was no stopping Boris once the toasting began. We had to toast David, you, me, Igor, the government of the United States, Mother Russia and, with some emotion, 'Woman'. At Boris's insistence, your piano was rolled into position so that I could play. 'We have heard the boys,' he said, dangerously red in the face. 'Now let us hear the man.' I agreed to play if everyone else agreed to dance. Furniture and carpets were moved to one side. Shoes were kicked off. The women adopted ballerina poses when I said I wished to play Chopin's waltzes. What no one realized was that I was going to play *all* of Chopin's waltzes. The women were soon exhausted. David and Igor leaned against the piano, drinks in hand, and watched me play. I have always played extremely well when drunk, a useful gift for the social musician. I could sense that the boys were not only impressed, but moved. I am such a terrifically good pianist, it amazes me even now.

When at last I finished playing, there was further hugging and kissing to get over with, followed by yet more toasting. Everyone was invited to spend the night, perhaps by me. Our conversations were of the deeply inebriated, friends-for-life variety. Mary smoked openly now; you did not show your disapproval.

There is only one bit of conversation that stands out in my mind from an otherwise vodka-soaked muddle. You and David and I stood next to the fireplace while Boris flirted with Evelyn, Igor nuzzled Charlotte, Penny and Mary compared notes.

'Well, my boy,' you said to David, 'this ought to make all the hard work seem worthwhile, what?' The sweep of your arm, one hoped, indicated something beyond a drawing room heaped with drunks. 'How does it feel?'

David did not reply. He was understandably wobbly on his feet.

You leaned forward with a drunken lurch and cupped a hand to your mouth. 'You showed our Russian friend a thing or two tonight. Lucerne *Aeneid*.'

'I beg your pardon?'

'*You certainly did*. Show him a thing or two.'

I thought this was pretty mean of you, considering that Igor had shown himself to be so magnanimous behind his public façade of arrogance and eccentricity.

'The time has come,' you said, 'to take him on his own ground. Into the breach, David. He's had his day. Now you will have yours. You will take the high ground of the concert hall stage. Devil take the hindmost!'

To my chagrin, David seemed not only to be listening to you – and understanding your slurred calls to battle – but *agreeing* with you. His normally sharp jaw had slackened from drink and exhaustion. Your faces were only centimetres apart when you put a hand on his shoulder, made the effort of focusing on at least one of his eyes, and said, 'Tell me one thing, David. Tell me just one thing. Tell me, David, how you feel about the Brahms Second.'

David's eyes brightened. 'Mister Brahms?' he said, after a quick wink at me. I remembered David's 'vision' of so many years ago. 'Mister Brahms is my favourite.'

'It's going to be a dream come true,' you said. 'For both of us. I will start planning in the morning. You, David,' you said, 'just have to practise so that you will play as beautifully as always. The world will be at your—'

'Geoffrey,' I interrupted. 'This may not be the time to make commitments we can't keep.'

'Nonsense,' you said, physically brushing me aside with the hand you weren't using to stroke David's shoulder. 'Now David and I must have a talk.' You guided him away, leaving me stewing in a rage and reaching out blindly for more drink.

Soon after his musical 'summit' with Igor Malechievich, David saw the light. I was able to convince him to grasp his destiny by the horns. I explained to him that he was born to play the Brahms Second, and that it would be my privilege to direct his performance. At last he was able to see the wisdom in this advice, and to overcome the nannying conservatism of La Valoise.

Here is sanitized fantasy. Absorbing the body blows of Your Chapter Eight, when the tables finally seemed to turn in your favour, I felt like a prisoner reading a confession he has no recollection of signing. I have tried, believe me, to rationalize your version of events as easier to relate, more sympathetic to your subject, more readily accessible to your readers. But how you could portray a dumb, drunken nod from David as a fundamental change of heart, I have no idea. I assure you that all David knew was that he wanted to waste as little time as possible removing Evelyn's clothes and his own, finding a door with a lock on it, and indulging in a pleasure that, I'm afraid, not even the Brahms Second at its best can provide. No doubt he achieved this aim, but not before you took him upstairs for a 'talk', from which he returned looking frightened and disturbed. I would not learn for many months that you had asked him to sign a piece of paper.

I am sorry that you strode back into your own drawing room to find me sitting next to your wife, fondling her left collar bone. We had all got a bit soppy, to tell you the truth, and Mary had so many interesting things to say about her barren life of socializing that I was unable to resist touching whatever fragrant part of her happened to be exposed. Igor and Charlotte were, amazingly, deep in conversation. Boris had decided to sit down, but wouldn't let go of Evelyn's hand. Penny, true to form, had long since found a bathroom in which to lie down.

180

After my successful pianistic deception, I was in the mood for the kind of misbehaviour which your book ascribes to my every waking hour. I had begun to feel an unmistakably mutual attraction between your wife and me. My failure to explore the tantalizing possibility of stealing your wife then and there can be accounted for by the gentlemanly instinct that made me search your house for my own wife, to make sure she hadn't hit her head on a washbasin and died. By the time I had found her, cleaned her face, and tucked her into bed, the party downstairs had dissolved. David and Evelyn had disappeared to put their more youthful and resilient bodies to good use; Igor and Charlotte soon followed their example; you and Mary were over by the piano arguing, probably about the rapt attention she had paid to me; Boris was being helped slowly from the room by your faithful Hopkins, a step at a time, muttering about his strong love for the English, even butlers.

When everyone else had gone to bed, Hopkins came back downstairs to ask if he could do anything to assist me. I said I would be grateful if he would help himself to a brandy and listen to me play the piano. He said he would consider it an honour. I played short, quiet pieces, and Hopkins clapped softly after each one. I spoke to him for a while about David's apparent conversion to your point of view, and Hopkins said he was sure it was all for the good, that Sir had David's best interest in mind and at heart.

I played some more; Hopkins clapped again and remarked on how well I played. One of the problems with butlers is that you can never tell when their praise is sincere. Now that I think of it, I often feel that way about non-butlers. One has to be so careful about ulterior motives, Geoffrey.

Your

PART THREE

THE DEATH
SPIRAL

Your

CHAPTER NINE

Your ambitious plan was to book David into twenty-five concerts in seven cities, at which he would perform the same programme each night: the Brahms Second Piano Concerto; a fifteen-minute breath-catching intermission; Chanat's *Death Spiral*. You could not have known that this project would take nearly two years to organize. The world, it turned out, did not owe David a platform. I would be the last to suggest that any of the delay was caused by European or American mistrust of your conducting credentials.

I was now a second-class passenger on the train of David's career. My job was to work with David on the Brahms, a task with which I was entrusted only because he would not agree to study without me. David's parents, who had never fully understood the balance of power between their son's two principal advisers, neared their retirement with the hope that he might soon begin to support himself. They knew that at the top level of concert pianism the financial rewards were staggering, but that the handful of élite players guarded their high ground like a fortress.

At thirty-eight, and somewhat strapped for cash on account of my not really having worked, ever, in my life, I had similar ideas for myself. The prospect of gainful employment reared up before me like a revolutionary workers' poster. I don't wish to think that my father died deliberately that year merely to spare me the drudgery of honest work, but die he did. My brother assumed my father's ludicrous title, threw himself with gusto into country life and distasteful right-wing politics, and tossed enough pocket money my way that I was able to cover my bets at the chess board and keep my kitchen pots bubbling.

I know that two years is not a long time in a rip-roaring biography, but in real life it includes a large number of wakings-up, of lyings back down again. I welcomed my renewed bachelorhood, and though I was neither emotionally disposed nor physically energetic enough to recreate the mood of my twenties, I cooked mouth-watering meals for sympathetic friends, and considered myself grown-up. David had decided that Evelyn was too 'possessive' of him, that she might just be 'prone to thick ankles', and that he would do better to find a nice French girl who was familiar with piano music and would therefore idolize him. This did not take long.

A new decade was upon us. You sent a card to David which read, 'The 1980s will be *your* decade!'

'Sure,' David remarked, when he showed me your postcard of Beethoven at his most severe. 'I'll turn thirty and start to go deaf and insane.'

'If you're lucky,' I replied. 'If you are very lucky indeed.'

I had now known this young man for nearly twenty years. By any standard, David was my best friend. I judged friends not just by how pleasant or loyal they were, but by how well they played chess, how well they played the piano, and how much they complimented me on my cooking: David ranked highest in all three categories. I loved his company. To the extent that I exerted the slightest influence on his life, I wanted the best for him.

Your book contains a wonderful photograph – taken during the two years you saw fit to ignore in your *Life* – that I too would have included in my *Death*. It depicts David and

186

me, as we strolled in the Jardin du Luxembourg. We are oblivious of the photographer, a fan of David's who began to follow him around after the appearance of his *Death Spiral* recording, secretly snapping away. In the picture, David and I are looking down at the gravel underfoot. We are deep in conversation. It is a beautiful image. Behind us, to one side, children are using wooden sticks to poke at their sailboats in one of the fountains. We are both wearing dark suits. Our ties form parallel diagonal lines in the breeze, and their angles nicely echo the sails of the heeling model yachts. Our outside hands are turned palms out, as if we are making the same point simultaneously. Our inside hands are shoved deep in our trouser pockets. We are walking in step. We are nearly the same height, but look like circus-mirror reflections of each other.

You used this photograph to illustrate the relationship between pupil and teacher during a period of fecund musical growth. The photograph backed up any number of words about the musician's intellectual analysis of his craft, the necessity of fresh air, the group effort involved in bringing out the best in individual performers.

I remember the moment with lightning clarity, and I know what we were discussing. We were not discussing the Brahms Second; we were not discussing nineteenth-century performing styles; we were not discussing music at all, in fact. We were discussing meat. We both wore expressions that would not have been out of place on the faces of Europe's deepest thinkers, I admit, but believe me: we were talking about meat – where best to buy, how best to cook, what with to wash down.

Your spies were at work in Paris, keeping an eye on me, watching for signs that I might be damaging your valuable investment. I wouldn't be surprised if David's photographer 'fan' was one of your paid-up Paris contacts, skulking about the parks and cafés, producing grainy night-time snaps of David not practising.

You visited us in person when your busy schedule allowed. As you neared the half-century of your impeccable innings, you had reached the level of celebrity that entitled you to pontificate on subjects far afield from music. With David's recording of the *Death Spiral* causing a satisfying stir, you felt obliged to remark upon United States foreign policy in Central America, not forgetting a conciliatory remark about the new government in Britain (the possibility of knighthood loomed even then). You discounted your Labour selection as a folly of youth – not forgetting a nostalgic word for your former comrades, lest they miraculously return to power.

Your public meetings with David were therefore publicity gold mines. I remember one interview in particular, in your hotel suite at the Ritz, when I thought you outdid yourself as a cosmopolitan man of the arts. You sat close to David, often extending a paternal arm as if to reassure him that the photographer wouldn't steal his soul. You fielded most of the questions posed by the earnest French journalist, intercepting many of those directed at David, as if the young virtuoso might exhaust himself with the effort of verbalizing his experiences or beliefs. A question about classical record sales was answered with a plea for expeditious reform of Jewish emigration laws in the Soviet Union; a question about Chanat was answered with a call to all thinking people to stand in solidarity with the mothers of Latin American torture victims. A question about your conducting and interpretation of Beethoven's Seventh was answered with a statement of your general loathing of racism and sexism in all of their manifestations, and a random mention of Hungary, 1956.

It took me some minutes to realize that you were giving exactly the correct answers. The journalist wrote everything down while nodding his head in energetic agreement. We were not really talking about Beethoven, not about Chanat, not about you, not about David; we were artists talking about the desire of the oppressed to be free, and the duty of the privileged free to link arms in solidarity with the oppressed. I could not have counted the number of times the Republic of South Africa was mentioned. It was a revelation to me, and it was beautiful.

David and I had a good laugh about it after you went to bed.

An artist, no matter how well he may be advised, holds his destiny in his own hands. That is my belief. He knows that at every juncture he must make choices, choices that will lead him closer to – or farther from – the firmament to which we all aspire.

Goodness. Destiny? *Firmament? WE?*

David now found himself at just such a crossroads, perhaps the most significant one in his life: Despite the bungling distribution job of the now defunct Profundo Records, David's Death Spiral *was a triumphant success . . .*

. . . sales: 2,850 . . .

. . . reviewers, so often merely polite to newcomers, with some exceptions greeted David like a relative long feared dead . . .

' . . . young Debrizzi's competent performance nearly – nearly – masks the wretchedness of Chanat . . . '

. . . he was the most talked-about young musician on Earth . . .

. . . on one particular morning in London, at any rate . . .

. . . he had made some money . . .

. . . three months' rent . . .

. . . and in his quiet, private way David basked in the well-deserved limelight of his first international coup . . .

That is your way of saying that David had his way with a certain number of admirers. Because he rarely went out on his own, he met these women through me, which must explain why in your Chapter Nine I sound like nothing more than a pimp.

'*There was a sizzling anticipation in the air,*' you feel compelled to write, '*as the day of David Debrizzi's adult début approached.*'

Nothing was sizzling, Geoffrey, except David when he practised. You might have chosen, at this point, to give your readers a better impression of what it was like to sit next to David when he played, to feel the piano itself as it sang under his touch. This is something no recording can convey, and not even live performance affords the listener such intimate contact with virtuosity. Since the age of six, David had possessed a relaxation and fluency that was a marvel to behold. When he practised he frequently talked or laughed while he played, narrating the music. His theoretical knowledge was highly sophisticated, and he derived a great deal of pleasure from critiquing the masters even as he performed them. It made him angry when he made mistakes; he would shout a one-syllable expletive in one language or another, and punish himself by returning to the spot and playing the phrase twenty-five times, no matter how boring this became.

His practice sessions, which usually lasted four hours, were intense and uninterrupted. In our nearly twenty years together I had managed to instill an extremely sober work ethic in David, which meant that he never simply went through the motions at the keyboard. From one note to the next, he expected progress, and he did not expect progress to advance mysteriously, of its own accord, without sweat and pain. Even a pianist of your limited ability will know the feeling of frustration that has to be endured and overcome for strides to be made. David struggled with the same block, but at an almost inconceivable level of musical and technical profundity.

Go to your piano, Geoffrey. Place your hands above the keys. Now play an arpeggiated C-major chord. Whoops! It's

Bach's First Prelude, isn't it? Go ahead and play it through. Play the first fugue, if you like. Isn't that fun? Did you do a good job? Now. Imagine playing the rest of the Forty-Eight, at one go, perfectly, from memory, with *inspiration*, so that everyone who hears it is amazed. A mite daunting, what? Yes. And now imagine performing that nearly incredible feat *because you have to*. That is only the beginning of what we had trained David Debrizzi to do; I don't think a brief, specious reference to 'sizzling anticipation' quite gets David's phenomenal accomplishments and potential across to your readers.

I make the same complaint about your treatment of David's adult love-life. I know that no biography is complete without in-depth analysis of the subject's sexual orientation, desires and obsessions, conquests and humiliations. In most cases, if only to make the material interesting, sexual initiation, deviation and experimentation must take precedence over long-term affairs or marriage; these events are then strung out into the biographer's unquestioning psychological analysis that is presented at the altar of history. In the lives of historical figures (Brahms comes immediately to mind; according to you he slept with Clara – she 'forced' him), where documentation is thin on the ground, we attach huge importance to mere shards of information. Napoleon, thanks to a random shred of hearsay evidence, is considered for all time to have been obsessed with filth and foul odour. Did it ever occur to anyone that because Napoleon, returning from a long journey, was himself so filthy and smelly that he wanted not to offend Josephine upon arrival?

The sex-lives of figures important enough to warrant biography are almost invariably 'abnormal'. Logic therefore dictates that: 1) we are all sexually abnormal; 2) accomplished and powerful people automatically become sexually abnormal; 3) one has to be sexually abnormal in order to become accomplished and powerful; 4) biographers are full of Freudian baloney.

We are pretty sure, after reading your Chapter Nine, that David practised a 'deviancy' of some kind. No doubt

191

there were legal reasons for not being too specific on this matter, and sex is, after all, most titillating when left to the imagination. But in only one page you employ all of the following verbal hedges: 'I rather think that'; 'shall we say'; 'was often thought to be'; 'not altogether unlikely that'; 'might in many cases amount to'; 'evidence might tend to indicate'; and 'experts agree'.

I believe that only I, having been there, could possibly sort out what you are implying about David's sex-life. Your general readers will jump to their own vaguely-informed conclusions. Your reviewers argued back and forth, and decided that their own newspapers' libel insurance would not cover detailed speculation on the matter. Only I know how thin and disconnected is the thread of evidence you used to extrapolate the tapestry of David's oh-so-vital sexual proclivities.

It was going to be a hot night in Paris. David and I were expecting a visit from you, and had loosely agreed to meet you for dinner. David and I emerged from my house, starving and frustrated, after a difficult afternoon arguing about the Brahms. We'd had a tiff. We blinked into the evening sunlight, coughed in the fumes, stretched our limbs, gave each other a good looking over to see if reconciliation might be in order.

'You're a bastard,' said David, who could never say such a thing without grinning.

'Only trying to help. You can't expect to play Brahms without feeling slightly ... slightly *underprivileged*. You looked and sounded haughty to me. That isn't the way I see Brahms.'

'The piece is beautiful. Who cares about Brahms's psyche, when the music sounds so good? I'll be haughty if I want to be haughty.'

'Be my guest.' I made a face designed to caricature David's expression as he had played the climax of the first movement: the look of a man, to put it bluntly, undergoing orgasm with a woman not his wife while listening to Puccini at terrific volume.

David gave my shoulder a little punch. 'You're crazy. That's not the way I'm playing.'

'Think about it next time.'

'Let's get a drink before I fight you. I want to play a game of chess before we see Geoffrey.'

No matter what you say, David was not a hermit. He joined me at the Père et Fils at least twice a week, and enjoyed chatting with my friends there. On the evening I have in mind, we sat in our shirtsleeves playing a game of chess, drinking beer, smoking – in other words, simultaneously enjoying roughly one third of all the pleasures life has to offer. Perhaps owing to our little disagreement during the afternoon's practice session, we played chess in silence, with murderous intensity. To my surprise, I was able to squeeze David's black pieces into a diabolical defensive bind by move sixteen. This happened so rarely that it only steeled my resolve to crush the life out of him. David fought with valour and cunning, bit his lower lip in concentration, tried to throw me off the scent of victory with a dummy knight sacrifice, occupied some of my resources with a pawn scurrying suicidally down the queen-side edge of the board, traded down as best he could, and resigned only when he was satisfied that he could not force a draw against my three-pawn advantage.

I was astonished to see that David was really quite angry. God knows I had lost enough chess games against him without the slightest show of bad sportsmanship, so it annoyed me that my fluke victory should be met with a hostile glare and a dismissive wave of his hand, as if I had cheated. Cheating, I don't have to remind you, is impossible in chess.

'You really are a bastard,' he said, for the second time in one day. He was not grinning this time.

'Yes,' I said. 'I *smashed* you. I was merciless. I made you feel pain.' I was rightly proud of myself, but obviously joking; I thought my sarcastic tone would snap David out of his childish funk. 'You never had a hope after my bishop to queen five. Would you like to replay that part? See if there was anything you could have done?'

193

David raised a hand and only just managed to restrain himself from sweeping the remaining pieces off the board.

'Relax, David. Let's have a drink.'

David was speechless with anger. He could not look at me. It was hot on the pavement outside the Père et Fils. The noise and smoke from rush-hour traffic must have contributed to his foul temper. I could see sweat soaking through his shirt. His eyes glared at the chessboard. He seethed for some time, grinding his teeth and rubbing his palms on his trouser legs.

'It's the Brahms, isn't it,' I finally said. 'Isn't it? You can't be so upset about a chess game, glorious and decisive as my victory may have been.'

'Pfff,' said David.

'I see.'

I had never known David to be so uncommunicative. Partly through my influence, I have to say, David had grown up knowing how to argue his own defence. He had a useful sense of superiority, and tended to sweep aside the irritations of life's small setbacks. He knew his own worth, but at the same time he had a healthy respect for the trials of other peoples' lives. After all, David had survived a childhood of exceptional academic and musical achievement without losing the sympathy and esteem of his peers, and without making a martyr out of himself. Because his silent anger was so out of character, I continued in the same flippant, sarcastic tone.

'We could play another game,' I said. 'I'll lay you knight odds.'

Without looking at me, David signalled our waiter and ordered a glass of wine for himself. I had to order my own. I teased him a little longer, certain he would come around. The sun had gone down, but a choking heat still clung to Paris. I asked David if he fancied a special dinner to raise his spirits. I described, in what I thought was enticing detail, the hot-weather menu I had in mind. I was determined to wheedle him out of his bad mood, and not to lose my patience. I also wanted to beat him at chess again.

When at last David looked me in the eye, it was not to melt into the expression of friendship and apology for which

194

I had hoped; he squinted at me like a gun-slinger and formed a devilish line of sarcasm with his lips.

'You,' David hissed, 'can play white again.'

Under normal circumstances, an angry chess player is a reckless chess player. In the state David was in, I thought I might thrash him yet again, and I did not intend to take prisoners. We hurriedly set up the pieces, and I launched into the same opening I had used to such effect in our previous game. David followed right along, leading up to the tricky spot that had resulted in his defeat. I was reminded of the way Igor Malechievich first retreated, then started all over again in the last movement of the *Appassionata* at the Salle Thierry: 'Pardon me,' Igor had said. 'I will start again.' In much the same way as Igor had heightened the tension in his performance by boldly building up to the troublesome section of the piece, David seemed to play his moves from memory, smoking impatiently, waiting for the moment in the game when he would deviate from disaster.

He chose move fifteen to alter the sequence of the previous game, and just as Igor had effortlessly negotiated the last section of the sonata, David had thought through his new strategy well before we reached that point in the game. I took my time in responding. The specifics of the game would not interest a layman such as yourself, even if you could comprehend them; suffice it to say that during the next five moves – that is, until David forced a vicious pin on my strongly centred knight – I have never thought so deeply about chess, and never felt so utterly powerless to stem the tide of defeat.

When my fate was beyond doubt, I played a few stalling moves so that I could prepare the smile and handshake with which I would graciously accept defeat. David had not looked up from the chessboard since we had begun our second game. I almost thought I could hear growls from his side of the table, like a wild animal tearing the flesh off the carcass of its fallen prey.

My gracious acceptance of defeat did not come off as I had hoped. I extended my hand across the table, smiled as warmly as a humiliated chessman can.

David did not look up. 'You resign, then?' he said.

'Of course I do, David.' With my left hand I laid my king on its side, a trite formality we normally did not employ. 'What a superb continuation,' I said. 'A brilliancy.'

Still not looking at me, David pushed back from the table, plucked his jacket from the back of his chair, slung it over his shoulder, and walked away. I was left with my right hand hanging limply over the chessboard.

I had experienced numerous scenes of this kind with women, but never with a man, and certainly not with David. I was more puzzled than worried, and thought at first that I would let him walk off his anger on his own. I watched him stride quickly away from me. He dodged oncoming pedestrians, and accidentally flicked a young man's shoulder with the tails of his jacket. I could sense his scowl right through the back of his head.

While I could not believe that his little tantrum amounted to a real falling out between us, I decided that I ought to follow him. I thought it might not be too late to salvage a pleasant dinner, even if you managed to join us. I left some money on the table, under the base of a glass. The chessboard belonged to the café. Jacket in hand, I walked down the hot and crowded pavement in the direction he had gone.

I searched ahead of me for David, who should not have been hard to spot. I craned my neck above a particularly dense pack of summer tourists, and when I still could not see him I accelerated into a quasi-trot. Unused to physical exercise, I soon found myself straining and panting and breaking into a most undignified sweat. Hoping none of my friends would see me in this state, I kept up a swift pace until I spotted David in the distance, making for the Seine.

I made up more ground, then stopped and leaned against a lamp-post to catch my breath. I cursed my lack of physical fitness, patted my pockets for cigarettes, lit one, then pressed on.

I guessed that David would head for his current girlfriend's flat – to vent his anger, to complain to her about me, about chess, about Brahms. David had finally found himself a

196

musician for a lover, a bright young oboist named Anne. I admired David's open-mindedness in putting up with an oboist as a girlfriend; oboists are almost always horrible, nasty little people, who look ridiculous when they puff out their cheeks, clamp their sucked-in lips on their double-reeds – all leading up to nothing more than an adenoidal whine. Anne made up for this handicap by being pretty, by being well brought-up, and by never requiring David to watch or hear her play. For all he had to know, she might as well have been a cellist.

I did my best secret-agent routine, stayed at least two blocks behind, skulked along close to the wall, paused occasionally behind a tree trunk and peeped out to make sure the coast was clear. I expected David to cross the river at the Pont Neuf; instead he stopped and sat down at a filthy, ill-lighted café in a side street near the Place St Michel. I concealed myself behind a parked van, off to David's right where he could not possibly see me, and I watched him.

A fatigued waiter limped up to the table and took David's order without looking down at him. David threw his jacket over a chair, leaned back, leaned forward again, then dropped his head into his sweaty hands. He remained in that pose of despair until long after the waiter had come and gone with what looked like a glass of tap water. He looked up again with bleary eyes, grasped the glass of water, and drained it. He replaced the glass on the table top, and then, in a slow and deliberate movement I shall never forget, turned his torso in my direction, extended his long right arm, and pointed his index finger directly between my eyes.

David's eerie gesture paralysed me. I didn't know whether I ought to approach him or flee. He held his arm aloft for so long that the waiter re-emerged from the café to take a closer look at the water-drinking lunatic. To spare David the embarrassment of being evicted, I cleared my throat and walked into the open. He lowered his hand, which was a good sign; then jumped to his feet and walked away, which was not. I pressed ten francs into the waiter's hand, and followed.

I hoped with all my heart that my ridiculous pursuit would not evolve into a foot race. As far as I could remember, I had not 'run' since 1955, at thirteen years of age, when the older brother of my delightful *petite amie* caught us necking on the back lawn of his house in Versailles, and decided to invoke his traditional protective rights. That he did not catch me had less to do with my athleticism than it did with his recently fractured left leg, but it was a close thing and I resolved never again to exert myself unless the honour of a woman was at stake.

David seemed to be limping. He crossed narrow streets without regard to traffic. He bumped against parked cars. He tripped on curbs. I searched my mind for what could possibly have affected him this way, having decided that Brahms – let alone my wicked chessboard killing – could not have made such an even-tempered young man so angry. Our afternoon's practising, while full of heated discussion, had not seemed volatile enough to deserve this reaction. Gasping for air, I was in no position to think clearly about the matter.

David made no serious attempt to escape from me. He headed away from the river now, back in the direction of my neighbourhood. It occurred to me that not one of the people who swerved to avoid him on the pavement could have any idea that this deranged and dangerous-looking man was *the* David Debrizzi, *the* champion of the Gaston-Robert competition (France's most promising young pianist!), *the* musician responsible for resurrecting at last that great Frenchman, Chanat. They quite understandably thought David was another drunk among the many who stumbled into their paths.

We were just down the street from my flat, separated by two blocks, when David suddenly stopped walking. He leaned a shoulder against a wall and bowed his head. At that point I thought he might have conquered his fury. I moved closer, expecting that at any moment he would turn around, turn on his famous grin, and burst out laughing. That would have been nice. When I was within earshot I stopped, and uttered a hopeful 'David?'

198

It was a heartbreaking sight. David turned his face to the wall, put his fists up to his temples, and began to tremble and heave as if in tears, which proved, actually, to be the case. Once again I was reminded, with a stab of pity and remorse, of past fallings out with women friends.

I went up to him and leaned my back against the wall – partly to appear relaxed, but mostly to regain my breath. I could hear that David was in that stage of tears – if women were anything to judge by – when interruption would have been counterproductive. He would have to cry it out, like sweating a fever. I smoked a cigarette and nodded good evening to passers-by. I listened as David's sobs became increasingly verbal.

'*Merde* . . . ' was the word he inevitably chose to express his anguish and embarrassment. '*Merde* . . . '

'It's all right, David,' I said at last, although 'it' was nothing of the kind. 'It's all right.'

Still leaning against the wall, I extended my hand and placed it firmly on his shoulder. Predictably, he shrugged it off. He needed more time. I passed the next few minutes listing to myself the reasons why I felt like joining him in a good cry. When I saw David shudder and heard him sigh, I thought I should attempt another soothing word or two.

'Are you feeling better now?' I asked him.

'Go away.'

'I see.'

'Go *away*.'

'I'll go away if you want.' I let this surrender hang in the air for a moment. 'Look, you could come over to my place and sit down for a while. A chat might do you good as well.'

'I don't want . . . to chat.'

'We could listen to music. There are some things I want to . . . '

'Not . . . *music*.'

He was off again, rather noisily.

'Hey, there,' I said. 'Come now.'

I really couldn't bear this. I suppose parents have to put up with it all the time, but not when their children have grown up and moved away. Only piano teachers get the really *good* emotion.

'There,' I said again. I put an arm around his shoulder. We were facing the wall together like a pair of prisoners about to be executed. Sure enough, there was a plaque on the wall at chest level: '*Ici est tombé . . .*'

David struggled half-heartedly, but I gave his shoulder a squeeze and he seemed to relax somewhat. A few more cheerful words of comfort from me, and he had stopped sobbing. With a great sigh he turned away from the wall, then leaned back against it, and rubbed his eyes and cheeks with his palms.

'What is it, David,' I said. 'Tell me what it is.' I lit a cigarette and handed it to him. I had decided that something must have gone wrong with Anne. Oboists can be so *shitty*.

'That chess game,' David said. 'My God.'

'I was magnificent,' I said.

'Pfff.'

'Oh come on. I'm only kidding. Tell me, has something gone wrong with Anne?'

David turned and looked at me for the first time. 'Anne? What could be wrong with Anne?'

'I simply thought . . . never mind.'

'Have you got something against Anne? You don't like her much, do you.'

'Well, having only met her two or three times . . . '

'She knows you hate her.'

'Hate her? She's marvellous. The oboe, on the other hand,' I waggled my hand in the air, 'is not so marvellous.'

'You are *so* unfair.'

'This is wisdom, David. Wisdom. I am only warning you. Oboists are not suitable companions for life.'

'I'm not going to marry Anne.'

'That *is* a relief.'

David flicked his cigarette into the gutter and folded his arms. A few strands of hair were stuck to his moist cheek; if he had been a woman I would have brushed them back behind his ear. We leaned against the wall, shoulder to shoulder. It was now nearly dark on the street, while overhead the sky retained a reassuring summer paleness.

David exhaled deeply, and shivered. 'I'm sorry about this,' he said. 'I really am.'

'Nonsense.'

'No, this is silly. *Burr.*'

'Put on your jacket.' David did so. 'Are you feeling all right? You don't have a chill?'

'I'm fine. I suppose I ought to explain.'

'Only if you want to.'

'It's very hard to say.' David inhaled in preparation for a longer sentence. 'Would you understand if I told you that I feel bored and frightened at the same time?'

'That's how soldiers feel. Why shouldn't you?'

'What do you know about soldiers?'

'Just trying to be helpful. Bored and frightened, right?'

David pulled a handkerchief from his pocket and blew his nose. 'Right,' he said, sniffling.

'Let me see if I can guess. You've been playing the piano for twenty years.'

'Right.'

'And you don't have much to show for it.'

'Right.'

'Except that you can play.'

'Right.'

'The concerts are coming up, and that scares you.'

'Right.'

'It's the vision of Mister Brahms all over again.'

'Yes.'

'You want to do well, but on the other hand you don't know why it matters.'

'Yes.'

'In the last analysis you just want to get out there and get it over with.'

'Absolutely. I don't want to talk anymore. I want to play. I want to know if I'm any good or not.'

'Does that just about sum it up?'

'Just about.'

201

'What else, then?'

David breathed in deeply through his nose, and looked up at the sky. I studied his profile as he prepared to speak, and I suddenly thought, *He has the kind of face that doesn't grow old.*

'I can't say it.'

'Oh, do.'

'All right, then, Pierre, I will. I've had too much time to think. Together you and I have intellectualized the whole thing.'

'The music?'

'That too. I meant . . . I meant my *life.*'

'I don't know if that is necessarily a bad thing.'

'Oh, it's bad all right.'

'How so?'

'Because I've had time to look closely at the situation – that's the boring part.'

'And the frightening part?'

'The frightening part is, *I don't want to end up like you.*'

One of the formative experiences in Chanat's life was the death of his little sister, Edwige. My guess is that she died of leukaemia. Chanat was only sixteen at the time, but already he showed signs that the burdens of the world were his in quite a personal way: he blamed himself for his little Edwige's death; he thought he had killed her with unnatural love. For the rest of his life he wore a locket around his neck containing a sprig of the little girl's hair. He became romantically involved with only one woman, his wife; she bore a strong resemblance to his sister, and was also named Edwige.

Chanat dedicated his career to the memory of his sister. When he moved to Paris in 1833, he was a twenty-three-year-old virtuoso on a grand romantic mission. He wanted to meet Mendelssohn. He wanted to talk about sisters. He wanted to be discovered, and offered up to Liszt's glorious salon world.

'Never before,' wrote Mendelssohn to Chopin, 'have I met such a repellent little man. When at last I was able to convince

Chanat to go . . . feigning illness . . . I still sensed traces of him clinging to my clothes.'

Chanat was never popular with the gang. If Mendelssohn found him 'repellent', Liszt thought him 'defective', and Chopin confessed, in a letter home, to an 'untoward hatred' of the new arrival. Others in the magical coterie of virtuosi seem to have conspired to prevent Chanat from enlisting pupils, in an effort to force him into poverty and out of Paris.

There was nothing they could do about his playing, however. The greatest night of Chanat's life was undoubtedly when he performed at Monsieur Pantin's gallerie, sponsored by Valéry Gorrianquoitre himself. As the expectant audience began to gather, and as Chanat waited patiently in a chair near his piano, a murmur began to circulate among the guests. Chanat looked up and saw women whispering excitedly, men looking concerned. It transpired that there in the audience, in clumsy disguise, were Liszt, Chopin, Thalberg and possibly two or three other bright lights of the day. They had all dressed in hats or beards or other crude camouflage, independently of each other. What a sight it must have been to see some of the greatest musicians in history scurrying for the door, finding it blocked, and trying to re-enter the hall with some semblance of dignity. In their shame, they watched Chanat's performance. Their surviving diaries all contain references to that night, written in the fire-and-brimstone prose those chaps preferred; all except Liszt admitted to having been transported and amazed by Chanat's playing. Liszt went only as far as to say that he was 'alarmed'.

In public, the big boys wrote glowing praise of Chanat's playing. How could they not? Everyone else had seen him too. Chanat's tone and technique seem to have resembled Chopin's, but where Chopin was sometimes diffident, Chanat was able to soar to Lisztian heights of *Sturm und Drang*.

For three years, Chanat basked in their approval. Society opened up for him. Students came to call. He saved enough money to send home a sufficient sum to have a gaudy monument built above his sister's crypt – it still stands. If ever a man of Chanat's disposition can be said to be happy, it was during those three years. He met and married his sister's namesake. He performed on a par with the greats. His compositions were met with suitable bafflement and outrage.

Chanat must have been dizzy with excitement. An existing sketch of Chanat, drawn during this period, shows the virtuoso sitting in a heavy wooden armchair, his pudgy legs crossed, his round face alight, his balding head aglow. His hands, folded in his lap, are blurred by the artist; he must have been fidgeting during the long sitting. It is a portrait of a tentatively happy man.

In 1836 Chanat suffered the first reversal in a series of setbacks that would stretch all the way to the pathetic ending of his life in a virtually unbroken continuum of bad luck. Chanat was caught in the arms of a pupil – 'Little Celeste', as he called her in his diary. Celeste was not so little: she was a middle-aged widow, but scandal cut deep in that hypocritical age. His mortified wife took her young son Emile by the wrist and dragged him home to mother.

Chanat began to feel himself ostracized. He lost all of his female students and most of the male ones. Concerts began to fall through. A fragile man, Chanat was not long in suffering the symptoms of ill health that were required behaviour among romantics at the slightest sign of adversity. For months he did not compose a note, and for all we know he may not have touched the piano. He had spent so much money on the monument to his sister that he could no longer afford food. What kept him going at all was the optimistic notion that his colleagues, especially the grand womanizer Liszt, would leap to his aid. While he waited, he did his best to appear on the boulevards only when immaculately groomed and dressed, but suitably wan and dissipated. He sat at cafés and restaurants ostentatiously *not* eating, and drinking only water or lemonade. Every now and then he slowly slurped a bowl of cabbage soup. When he was forced to give up his apartment and sell his Pleyel piano, Chanat knew that Liszt and the others would soon spring to the rescue. He thought the appropriate gesture would be a benefit concert, a convivial evening of virtuosity starring all the greats, and ending, perhaps, with one of Chanat's own patented improvisations. He could see the scene in his mind. He could see the diamonds and emeralds sloping over the aristocratic collarbones of Paris society. He could see a standing ovation that included Liszt himself. He could see Edwige and Emile at the back of the room – late arrivals – beaming with pride and forgiveness. He could see that bitch Celeste . . .

Nothing ever happened. Chanat was betrayed by the Brotherhood of virtuosi. They turned their backs on him; in fact they seemed to revel in his fall. One fewer pair of hands to gum up their glorious works, they seemed to be saying – one less sun in the sky to obscure their exploits.

Of course, we will never know what the Brotherhood really did or did not do to help or sabotage Chanat. Biographers like you must draw their own conclusions. My method would be to take Chanat's diaries at face value: if Chanat *felt* betrayed, then betrayed he most certainly was.

I recall and relate this story because it was what sprang to mind when David said what he did: '*I don't want to end up like you.*' I felt betrayed. His words were so stark, and so completely out of the blue, that I experienced that rare sensation of having one's knees half-buckle. It made me see how a man might write a piece of music like the *Death Spiral*. I have never been married long enough to find out, but I imagine that I felt like the joyfully ignorant and devoted husband who discovers that his wife has not just had an affair, but a long – no, a very, very long – enjoyable, profound affair: a secret second marriage, as it were.

I know that I over-reacted, but there is no denying strong emotion. David was looking me in the eye, the way people are wont to do when they have laid their cards on the table. His clear blue eyes projected nothing but pity. He could not have been prepared for my reaction, which was to burst into tears. This might be expected in a friend, a lover, a parent, a child; this is not what a young man wants to see in his piano teacher.

I am certain that you have never cried in front of someone else since cricket days, so you will not know what I mean when I say that *not wanting* to cry is a guaranteed precipitator of further tears. I was a wonderfully helpless man, reduced through worry and shock to a blubbering, speechless wreck. From what I could see through the waterworks, David's expression had changed considerably: what had been stony confrontation was transformed into panicked concern. He could not believe what he saw. Pierre La Valoise – stalwart teacher and companion, reduced to shuddering sobs.

'Pierre,' he said, almost impatiently, not knowing what to do with his hands. 'Pierre, please. I didn't mean it.'

'It's . . . my . . . turn,' I managed to say. What an emotional evening we were having.

Struck by several more spasms, I supported myself against the wall to avoid actually falling down. This must really have shaken David, whose previous tantrum was now considerably dwarfed by my own, so that the next thing I knew he had me under the arms, propping me up and telling me he was sorry.

'I'm sorry,' David said, sensibly enough. 'I mean, I am really, *really* sorry. It isn't at all what you think. I was only saying . . . ' David was having difficulty holding me up.

'What . . . were . . . you . . . saying?'

'Oh, for God's sake. I was unhappy. I said . . . I said a version of the truth, if you will. We'll talk about it later.'

I was so pathetic. Sobbing away, leaning against David. He must have felt truly awful. He must have been thinking that after all I had done for him, he had said something so foolish that it might damage our friendship forever.

I am, as you know, a Frenchman; nevertheless, I was embarrassed. I could not stop crying, just *exactly* like a woman, and it was not a pleasant experience. No doubt David was just as embarrassed as I was, but he responded, in the end, by abandoning excuses and giving me a manly hug. Well, not so manly by your standards. He hugged me like a father and brother and son combined, and like all of those I felt extremely good, right away. Our day was about to end well, with understanding and forgiveness. Our day *would* have ended that way, and your Chapter Nine would not read the way it does, full of cautiously worded implications, had it not been for . . .

'I say, you chaps!'

And then you were upon us.

'A bit, er, late, am I?'

David and I, tearful and still leaning against a Parisian wall with our arms around each other, tried to focus our eyes as you emerged from the shadows.

'Geoffrey,' we said in unison. 'How . . . nice to see . . . you.' There was a certain amount of hiccuping and throat clearing and tie adjusting as we separated from our clinch and prepared to shake your hand.

'Now then,' you said, making an effortful show of having seen nothing whatsoever of biographical interest. 'Too late for dinner. Where for drinks?'

You stood between us like a boxing referee. You smiled insanely at each of us in turn, and put an arm around David as if wanting a piece of the perceived action.

'I know a little place,' you said. 'Mustn't keep you long, though. I need my rest. A frightful journey today. Practically crash-landed at Charles de Gaulle. Reminded me of the war, ho ho. Come with me. Off we go. Comb your hair, David.'

Walking between us, with an arm around each of our shoulders – because we were so much taller you had to walk like an orang-utan – you guided us back to the Père et Fils, while keeping up a cheerfully inane monologue about your recent productions in Italy. We sat at the same table where David and I had played our two chess games in the rush-hour heat. Our emotional circuit of the Left Bank ended where it had begun.

You ordered champagne, with grand gestures, in your appalling accent.

'I have news,' you said. 'It is time for us to gloat. Neither of you looks very well. I am about to cheer you up.'

'We're ready,' David said. 'Tell us.'

'A drink in hand, first, don't you think? Tell me all your news in the meantime.'

'No news,' I said.

'Correct,' said David.

'I rather doubt that,' you said, forming that fantastically prissy shape of mouth that has been captured so often on film.

'Concentrating on the Brahms,' David said, to say something, anything. 'It seems to be going well. I do love the piece. Although sometimes my interpretation is "haughty".'

'That *is* good to know. Ah, here are our glasses. Gentlemen, a toast.'

Reluctantly, we raised our glasses.

'Cheers,' you said. 'To David. To all of us. The dates are set. We begin in London. Six weeks from Thursday. The machinery is in place. Or in motion? Cheers.'

'Cheers,' we replied.

'At long last,' you said.

'At long last.'

'And about time, too.'

'And about time, too.'

'Chanat lives.'

'*Vive Chanat*.'

'Cheers!'

We drank. We drank again. There was an uncomfortable silence, which David and I tried to fill by lighting cigarettes and pretending to be lost in the joys of smoking.

'This isn't the reaction I'd expected,' you said. 'Really. It must be relief and gratitude that makes the two of you frown that way. Am I right? Or am I . . . ' you smacked your lips. 'Or am I missing something?'

'Relief,' said David.

'Gratitude,' I said.

'I thought so, yes.'

The evening petered out. We wandered home in three separate directions. You never mentioned the incident, not until now, not until your Chapter Nine: here it is in my hands, lawyer-proof but plain as can be; a reviewer's talking point; Sir Geoffrey Flynch at his most incisive.

'There is no artistry without excess,' is one of your home-brewed apophthegms. That day, off the Rue de Rennes, eight years ago, with a flippant 'I say, you chaps!', you found your excess, and you used it like a cudgel.

Your

CHAPTER TEN

'Art is never anyone's *fault*,' Chanat once wrote. 'Not the patron's for supporting it; not the critic's for adoring it; not the artist's for creating it. Art enters the flux, and is crowned or dethroned in the total absence of rules or standards . . . Progress in art is a fallacy. My aim is expression, and, knowing what I know, acceptance is irrelevant.'

Yes, well, Chanat *was* a bit of an idiot, and never had the German knack for aphorism. Still, of all the composers I have studied, he strikes me as one of the most self-contained.

'Chanat was *integral*,' David once pronounced, prompting me to change the title of my still-unpublished biography to *The Integral Chanat*.

Chanat spent the last thirteen years of his life persuading his wife and son to return to him, and building up to the frenzy of composition that gave us the *Death Spiral*. He succeeded on both counts, and never said an unkind word about anyone but himself in the process. You could learn a great deal from Chanat's example.

*

Your Chapter Ten covers the period of David's London concert in September, 1982, and what you erroneously call his first 'breakdown'.

> *I considered La Valoise's presence in London to be redundant and unnatural. I do not think that I exaggerate when I say that I could feel his unwelcome presence behind me in the auditorium as I put David and the orchestra through their paces. This alone would have been distracting enough, but La Valoise persisted in interrupting the rehearsals with unnecessary and, if I may say so, impudent commentary and advice. A conductor demands unquestioned authority; his is a dictatorial task. I doubt that anyone who was there on the first day of rehearsal, with the possible exception of David himself, disagreed with my decision to have La Valoise banned from the hall.*

You have made it sound as if I was sent back home to Paris while you and David continued the tour; that did not happen until later. Since the full-orchestra rehearsal time must have lasted a total of eight hours spread over two days, it isn't exactly as if I missed a great deal. I did not '*lurch off into the streets*' – no, I took one of London's bulky taxis straight to your house to pay my respects to Mary. The first thing she said to me, even before I told her I had been banned from the auditorium, was 'Give me a cigarette, darling.'

Mary – and she would forgive me for saying so – looked awful. Emanuel, who was then fifteen years old and living with you rather than with his unbalanced natural mother, was making great demands on Mary's patience, even though you made sure he spent as much time as possible in the care of the most expensive experts your educational system had to offer. He looked and acted more like Sarah than you, which should have given you a chilling premonition of misbehaviour to come.

Emanuel wanted to know who I was. When I told him I was a piano teacher, among other things, he said that, on the contrary, I was a 'peasant'.

'A peasant, Emanuel? Are you sure that is what you really mean? A *peasant*?'

Mary attempted to intervene. 'Emanuel has been studying feudal society, I believe.'

'He should have said "serf", then,' I said. 'Emanuel, you should have said "serf", not "peasant".'

'We are learning about peasants as well,' said your boy to your wife. 'And a peasant is what *he* is.'

'Do you say that because you think I speak in a strange way?'

'I know French accents,' said Emanuel. 'I *speak* French.'

'I find that very unlikely,' I said, a bluff-calling statement that had the desired effect of sending Emanuel into a foot-stamping rage, straight upstairs to his room.

With peace restored, I told Mary that the main purpose of my visit was to invite her to accompany me to David's concert, given that her husband would be occupied at the conductor's platform. She accepted. I then told her that I had been banned from rehearsals for offering suggestions.

'You weren't. He didn't.'

'It's true.'

'I don't want to excuse him,' Mary said, 'but Geoffrey seems to be taking this concert more seriously than any in ages. We've heard nothing around the house but the Brahms Second since I don't know when. Of course, he conducts in front of the mirror.'

'Don't we all,' I said.

'Yes, but with his shirt off? With the heat turned up until the windows fog? With . . . '

'I see, yes. He is high-strung.'

'You could say that.'

'It's best that I'm out of the way, then.'

Mary and I sat down to coffee and more cigarettes. I found it odd that a woman with such a busy social schedule, who entertained so frequently, who had so many friends, should

212

sit across from me and suck down cigarettes and gossip like a truant from a convent school. I could not help thinking that you had been neglecting her. We spent the whole afternoon together. We parted, as even innocent people will do, only because we expected your return, and knowing that we ought to keep our happy conversation to ourselves.

> *I am afraid that it is impossible in a work such as this one to leave all personal matters to one side . . .*

It is wonderful that you pretend to be making an exception to strict biographical standards at this point.

> *. . . but I must report that no sooner had I decreed that La Valoise was no longer welcome at my rehearsals, than the Frenchman began visiting my wife at my home, maliciously taking advantage of her good manners, and slandering me behind my back.*

The pathetic thing is that I never slighted you, not even slightly. I am not saying that I wish I had, but . . .

> *. . . La Valoise really had gone far enough. It was then that my vague desire to shunt him into the background of David's life became concrete purpose.*

Concrete purpose? As a Frenchman I would never dream of criticizing your choice of words, but . . .

> *La Valoise was an anchor. He was a caboose with brakes on. I had to cut him adrift.*

'Listen,' said Mary, your wife. 'Listen, Pierre, while you're here. We ought to try to have some fun.'
We were both about to turn forty. We were both, it has to be said, underachievers. I have taken friends and allies where I could find them. At my few, brief meetings with your wife, when in jest I publicly declared my love for her, I always

felt somehow *appreciated*. Perhaps she only wanted me for my cigarettes.

'Yes,' I said, in Mary's own spirit of ambiguity. 'We ought to have fun.'

By trying to make your readers believe that I attempted to seduce your wife, I really think you may have given them the strong impression that I succeeded. Was that what you intended? Is that what you think? Did Mary tell you so?

I suppose one of your initial bits of evidence was that when David protested my banning, and threatened to pull out of the concert if I was not allowed into the second day's rehearsal session, I replied, 'No no, David. Never mind. No no, I'll be just fine. Much better if I stay away. Carry on, chaps.'

Given that I have set myself the task of clearing up the errors of your *Life*, I suppose I ought to state categorically, right now, one way or the other, whether or not I actually . . . but that would spoil a delicious mystery for you. It amuses me to think that for all these years you have harboured a suspicion so nagging that you felt compelled to draw a public readership into so private a worry. I would hate to put an end to so fundamental an anxiety.

A few words on your rehearsal technique, which I felt privileged to witness before my unceremonious eviction. It is strange to think that I had never seen you conduct before, except on film. Musicians have a way of gossiping brutally about backstage matters, and I confess that I rarely heard a word spoken against you, much as I tried to solicit bitchiness from the few orchestral players I met who had laboured beneath your whipping baton. One English viola player, who was not the sort to complain, but who had a certain way with words, did once ridicule what he called your 'unctuousness and pretension', which he likened to 'a self-regarding film director bemoaning the inability of his actors to comprehend his genius.' Still, I never had much faith in viola players, who almost invariably toil under the severest inferiority complexes, so I was happy to see you in action for myself.

214

It is so important for the maestro to know what to wear to rehearsal, and I thank God I've never had to make such a vital sartorial decision. Most conductors opt for a relaxed, sitting-in-front-of-the-fire-with-the-wife look, carefully constructed so that when one's genius heats up, layers can be removed to reveal, at last, the great visionary armpit stains. Scarves, and even hats, are important, and symbolize an artistic fear of viral infection that Chanat would have understood completely. I was happy to see that you did not deviate too far from the norm. You entered, stage left, only after David and the orchestra had settled into their places and finished warming up. You bounced up to the podium to the click-click-click of their bows, wearing stove-pipe trousers, two or even three V-neck jumpers, a scarf around your neck, brand-new white tennis shoes, and no socks. You looked like a tourist on holiday in a climate too cold for the clothes he has brought along. Geoffrey, don't get me wrong: you looked *good*.

Your five-minute introduction of the soloist was an accolade sprinkled with French words and phrases, perhaps designed to give the orchestra the impression that David spoke no English. In our business it is desirable to be exotic. David himself, whose wardrobe had never varied much since I first began to influence his dress-sense, wore his usual dark suit, white shirt and dark tie. He would not have removed his jacket even in a Bombay heat wave. He sat stoically at the piano *sans* page-turner, *sans* music, and, soon enough, *sans moi*.

I was eager to hear your preliminary remarks about the Brahms Second, to find out how open you would be to David's views on the piece, and to see for myself if my orchestral mole had spoken the truth when he said that you conducted 'like a mosquito going in for the kill'.

'How many of you,' you asked the orchestra, 'did as I asked and listened to Mr Debrizzi's recording of the Chanat *Death Spiral*?'

Twenty-odd hands or bows were raised. If I am not mistaken there came a cat-call or two from the brass section.

215

'Yes, well, good,' you said. 'That's a start, anyway. Many of you will therefore have an idea of how great an opportunity this is to perform a truly stunning Brahms.'

David cracked his knuckles and drew a laugh. Even from my seat near the back I could see that he had developed a visual rapport with your one female cellist. Now, the cello is an instrument I approve of, from a romantic standpoint.

'Those of you who have not heard the Chanat are in for a treat.'

Oh, come on. You *hated* Chanat.

'But in the meantime it is our job to knuckle down to the Brahms.' You raised your baton. 'From the top, then, people?' Yes, you actually tapped the top of your music stand.

David played the spiky opening arpeggios without looking down from the swaying strokes of your baton. With the introduction over, his eyes noticeably widened as he was engulfed by the stirring sound of the orchestra at full volume. He was so struck by his first exposure to this sensation that his next entrance caught him sitting with his hands in his lap. There were titters from the brass section – brass players are, as you know, uncouth.

'That was very, *very* beautiful,' David said.

You waved your hands in the air to stop those musicians who had kept their noses in their parts and continued playing despite the lack of a soloist, and to silence the titters near the back. You were more embarrassed than annoyed.

'Really, David, I'm surprised at you. Let's play the piece, shall we?'

It was then that you removed a new affectation from your worn leather music case, a pair of half-moon reading glasses. You placed them on the tip of your nose and glared over them at the orchestra, then over your shoulder at David. He cleared his throat, apologized under his breath, and motioned self-consciously for you to carry on with your business. You kicked off the concerto for the second time, and David did not disappoint. You played the entire first movement through without stopping. When it was over, David yawned like a bored child and squinted into the gloom of the seats, looking

216

for me. It was as if he thought the rehearsal was over. He caught my eye and shrugged his shoulders.

'David!' you shouted. 'I am going to have to ask you to concentrate. We have *work* to do.'

Your tone of voice had me half out of my seat, ready to storm down the aisle like an assassin. I could not believe that you would speak this way to your soloist in front of other musicians. A conductor needs his authority, yes, but the soloist's role is precarious enough without the conductor's undermining his superiority. You were treating him like a little boy. Maybe you still thought of him that way.

I may have said something – or perhaps my sneer was so obvious that you could see it over the rims of your new glasses – because I distinctly remember being reprimanded. 'And I'll thank *you* to keep out of this,' you said.

I am certain I was not the only one in the hall to think that you were losing control. I said only one further sentence before you threw down your baton, jumped athletically from the stage, and strode up the aisle to where I was sitting so that you could ask me please to leave.

'I'm going,' I said.

'Good,' you replied.

'Oh, but one last thing.'

'Yes?'

'Your tempo.'

'What *about* my tempo?'

'It's perfect.'

I always like to storm out of places on a pleasant note.

I visited your wife. I crept out of your house by the back door when we heard your garage door opening. I met David, as previously agreed, in my hotel bar. I was not surprised to see him joined by the cellist, whose name was Barbara. I asked them how the rest of the rehearsal had gone. They said you had seemed rather tense. Barbara, who had worked with you before, said she thought you were putting inordinate emphasis on the Debrizzi concert – no offence to David, of course. Barbara was a victim of your London propaganda scheme, and therefore believed that you had raised David Debrizzi from birth as your own child.

Do you remember Barbara? She played the solo cello part in the third movement, and very well indeed. She may still be trying to make a living in London, so I should quickly add that she had nothing but the kindest praise for your conducting, your trim physique, and your . . . oh . . . your creative generosity. Yes, she worshipped you. She had only one criticism – and I know you would never hold this against a professional musician. 'He takes everything so seriously,' she said, 'that you'd think Brahms was the end of the world.'

'And what about David?' I asked her, fishing for compliments on my friend's behalf.

'David?' She was sitting shoulder to shoulder with him, and gave him a playful shove. 'David's *super*.'

'How nice of you to say so.' Then, with mock seriousness, I addressed David. 'Young man,' I said, 'you have more rehearsing tomorrow, and a concert in three days. I expect you to eat and rest properly so you don't make a complete hash of your performance and embarrass us all to death. Spend plenty of time in bed.'

'Right you are,' David said. He drained his glass and led the cellist away.

Did I rush out the next morning to see your wife when you and David went to your final rehearsal? Did I? No, I did not. Mary rushed out to see *me*. Our intention had been to take a walk, but after a quick look at wet and filthy London we settled on strong coffee and cigarettes in my hotel room.

'Geoffrey hates the idea of turning fifty,' was one of the things Mary said to me. 'He thinks he may not have achieved enough – can you imagine? He thinks his talents have been diluted, that he has worn too many hats. He says he wishes he could lead five lives simultaneously.'

'Sametimeously?'

'Yes, right.'

'How ambitious of him.'

Naturally I could not help taking the opportunity to ask what her husband could possibly make of a worthless ne'er-do-well like me.

'Geoffrey once said, "Pierre has squandered more talent than the rest of us put together have *used*."'

'What a generous thing to say.'

'I don't believe he meant it in a nice way. Also, he thinks you have suffered horribly – but perhaps I shouldn't bring that up.'

'Jacqueline, again. Do you know I can't remember Jacqueline's last name? He seems to be obsessed with my supposed early trauma. A man like Geoffrey needs a *reason* for what he perceives to be my failures.'

You will now be wondering whether or not this conversation took place in a haze of post-coital cigarette smoke. As someone who pretends to be a gentleman, I would never tell you even if it had.

Mary and I agreed again that she would accompany me to your concert. I assured her that I would not be welcome backstage, and convinced her to join me at the theatre bar instead. We would be alone, I said, because David's parents would not be coming to London; they would see enough of David's performing when we returned to Paris. In unison Mary and I told each other not to worry. It was only a concert, after all.

On the day of the performance I was allowed to spend the afternoon with David. He insisted on walking in the park, perhaps because you had expressly forbidden him from doing so, or from going outside at all. We walked bare-headed in the misty drizzle.

'My parents used to be the same way,' said David. 'They seemed to think I had a special vulnerability to disease. That was until I was about six years old. Geoffrey hasn't stopped being that way. I told him I thought I could play with pneumonia, if I had to.'

'Good for you.'

'Geoffrey is the one who will fall ill, if he doesn't stop worrying. At the second rehearsal Barbara and I thought he would collapse on to the stage during the third movement. He was waving his hands around as if he were trying to *fan* the music out into the hall. He kept shouting something about playing so softly that it was *deafening*. Do you have any idea what he could have meant by that?'

'Not a clue.'

'We all pretended to understand.'

'Probably best. Rehearsal time is short.'

'Afterwards he told us all that he could hardly stand the beauty of our playing, that it was a privilege to know us and to be in the same building with us, and that he knew we were going to give a good account of ourselves tonight. I don't think he noticed when one of the trombonists made a farting noise with his horn.'

'Poor Geoffrey.'

'Did you know he has a chauffeur?'

'I'd heard.'

'He drove me home after the rehearsal. I had planned to meet Barbara, but Geoffrey just swept me away. I could see he wanted to have an important talk.'

'And did you have an important talk?'

'Yes. More of a lecture. I was slightly embarrassed because the chauffeur was listening.'

'People like Geoffrey don't care about that sort of thing. What did he say to you?'

'At first, all kinds of nice things about my playing, about how good the orchestra sounds, about how there's *nothing to worry about*, in that very *worrying* tone of voice.'

'I remember it well. "*Relax!*"'

'That's right. But then he became serious and told me – you're going to hate this – he told me I shouldn't be "fraternizing" with members of the orchestra.'

'Barbara?'

'That's who he meant, yes.'

'Did you tell him you liked fraternizing Barbara? I mean *with* Barbara?'

'I hinted that I did. He said it wasn't right, and gave various reasons.'

220

'Which were?'

'He didn't say this in so many words, but I could tell he meant that it was demeaning, like sleeping with the servants.'

'That makes sense.'

'And he thought I would be distracted.'

'I would have thought that was the whole point of fraternizing. Especially with Barbara. I'll bet she's distracting as anything. I like Barbara.'

'She is. I like her too. When I said as much, Geoffrey started saying some very strange things about bull-fighters and boxers and one particular tennis player he used to know.'

'Let me guess. Sapping the masculine energy?'

'Correct. I mean, he didn't seem to think it was going to affect *Barbara's* playing. Or he didn't say so.'

'I hope you know that what he is saying is complete nonsense.'

'Give me *some* credit. Of course I know that. It's just that I didn't want to make him any more nervous than he already was. So I let his driver take me back to the hotel, and I called Barbara from there. Do you know, Geoffrey phoned every hour, on one pretext or another having to do with the concert, to check up on me?'

'Poor Geoffrey.'

'Poor Geoffrey? Poor *me*. The third call found me fraternizing pretty, uhm, heartily. I had to say he'd caught me in the shower. A cold shower.'

'Geoffrey's just an old lady.'

'I'm afraid you might be right.'

'Well, now I'll be an old lady and give you some advice of my own.'

'Go ahead. Just please leave Barbara out of it.'

'Barbara, or if necessary her equivalent, is at this stage more important than practising. Fraternize away. My advice concerns the Brahms.'

'Oh, that.'

'Yes, I know. Not as interesting as Barbara. But for three-quarters of an hour, tonight, you might as well try to make it shine.'

'If you say so.'

'I'm a little worried by the things I've heard Geoffrey say about the piece. It all sounds very solemn to me.'

'*Solemn*? Geoffrey thinks the piece is death itself. He goes on at length about sadness and regret and class anxiety.'

'*Class anxiety?*'

'Brahms's humble roots, I think he means.'

'Oh, for God's sake.'

'The third movement – Barbara's moment in the sun, as it happens – is supposed to be some kind of "death rattle", according to Geoffrey.'

'How nice for the audience. A death rattle and a *Death Spiral* all in one programme.'

'I take it you disagree with him?'

'Now, listen to me. Any piece of music, no matter the tempo, the key, the tonality, the harmonies – no matter how superficially quote unquote *sad* – is fundamentally joyful.'

'There's a thought.'

'It isn't my idea. It's Chanat's. But I think I mean it. Music equals joy. Period. If you sit down to the Brahms and you *look* solemn and you *feel* solemn and you tell yourself to *sound* solemn, you are just going to depress a lot of people and the music will die in the air. If you look joyful, and you feel joyful and you tell yourself to sound joyful, you are going to surprise a lot of people when you play them those supposedly heart-rending strains. That's how you get a feeling of triumph in music that can actually be communicated.'

'Do you know what else Geoffrey says?'

'What else does Geoffrey say?'

'That if we do it right, we'll be able to smell concentration camps.'

'My God.'

'And so will the audience, naturally.'

'I honestly think, David, that I wouldn't have to argue too long to convince you that what Geoffrey is saying is slightly unfair to Mister Brahms. Unless, of course, he means concentration camps in the *nicest possible way?*'

'I think he meant the saddest thing he could think of off hand, plus Brahms's being German.'

'Brahms, then, was a crypto-Nazi with class anxiety? This has gone far enough. I'm going to go straight over to Geoffrey's – look, you can almost see his house from here – I'm going straight over there to—'

'Relax, Pierre. As Geoffrey would say, "*Relax!*" I'll be joyful. Just you watch me being joyful.'

'Geoffrey was sick,' said Mary. 'It was awful.'

'I can never tell what the English mean when they say "sick". Did he . . . ?'

'All over the place. It was awful.'

'Actors do it all the time. I've done it. The stage is terrifying, we might as well admit it. Still, conductors should have the courage to be sick in secret.'

'At least it was while we were still at home. He looked better when he left for the concert hall, but he didn't say a word. He has a *case* for his *baton*, Pierre. This worries me.'

'How many orchestras has he conducted, really? Do you know?'

'He conducted often enough, years ago. But not everything worked out, you see. There are plenty of conductors to go around, some of whom are more . . . *focused* than Geoffrey. Recently his work has mainly been in Italy, as you know. But that has been directing, not conducting, so he has been able to stay in his hotel and vomit privately while the shows go on. He considers this concert an important step.'

'He may be right about that.'

'Have you seen David?'

'Yes. Just this afternoon. David will be fine. I sent him off to visit his new girlfriend, against Geoffrey's explicit instructions. Do you mind a very personal question? Something David said made me ask myself if Geoffrey enjoyed conjugal relations in the days preceding a concert . . . ? Just wondering.'

'Pierre! Of *course* I mind. Funny you should say "enjoy", though . . . No, we mustn't talk about that.'

223

We stood at the bar, keeping our voices down, amid a large crowd of well-disposed Brahms-lovers, and perhaps the odd connoisseur of Chanat. David's recording was something of a cult success. Dozens of people had brought albums to the theatre, and others had purchased them at the concession stand, hoping to have them autographed at the stage door. I could not look at the album cover's picture of David without feeling guilty: so many of the record's vinyl grooves belonged to me. At the same time I took pride in seeing Chanat billed just beneath Brahms on the programme, in knowing that I had played a part in initiating the first large-scale performance of the *Death Spiral* since Alexei Berliokov's rather disastrous attempt in the Twenties.

'You're looking pale yourself, Pierre,' Mary said.

'Not at all, my dear. I have no worries. I had a friend of mine inspect the piano this evening. Her name is Virginie. She was my tuner, and David's, for several years. Married an Irishman living in London. More of my expert matchmaking.'

'You do look out for David, don't you.'

'And why not?'

'I never know what to make of you . . . *boys*. Geoffrey says the most damnable things, sometimes.'

We were being nudged aside by people ordering last-second drinks at the bar. You will know how unpleasant it is to be treated with such disrespect when one considers oneself in some ways at the centre of the action.

'Tell me,' I said. 'I have to know.'

'I really shouldn't. It would be . . . all right, I'll tell you.'

'Only hurry. Seconds to go.'

'Simply that . . . oh, you're going to think I *care* about this sort of thing.'

'*What* sort of thing?'

'You and David. Geoffrey's last trip to Paris. He reported, or said, that he sort of more or less . . . *burst in* on you two.'

Electronic bells sounded in the foyer. It was time to enter the hall. Mary took my arm. We must have been a sight, Mary trying to look composed, in case anyone recognized her, as I leaned down and stage-whispered demands for clarification.

'Never mind,' she said. 'We'll talk later. Anyway, who cares what he thinks?'

'Who *cares*? Who *cares*? He's probably going to write it all *down* one day.'

We were both smiling now, on the off chance that some-one in the audience might take an interest in us as we gained our seats.

'Hush,' smiled Mary.

'Oh, no,' I said.

'What is it now?'

'It's that bloody Igor Doppelgänger Malechievich. Second row.'

'I've heard of *him*,' said Mary, forgetting through years of frantic socializing that she had entertained Igor and Boris in her home. 'What a stunning girl he's with.'

'I don't see Boris. That must mean he isn't here to cast a spell.'

Igor looked well enough, with his hair brushed back to emphasize the Mahlerian slope of his forehead. Members of the audience sitting near him cupped their hands and whispered into each other's ears not to look now, but there was the famous Igor.

I kept my nerves under control by trying not to think of the hysterical exhortations with which you were no doubt pummelling your musicians. I had told David to show up as late as possible just to make you that much queasier, and to spare him at least some of your irritating pep-talk. As the seconds passed I could not help feeling sorry for both of you, and suffering a sympathetic anxiety.

The orchestra walked on to the stage in an orderly procession. Barbara looked as if she had not had time to dry her hair. I almost had to close my eyes against the routinely depressing sight of union-scale, overworked, under-appreciated musicians dressed like undertakers, tuning for the millionth time to an antisocial oboist's A, their minds far away on gas bills, school bills, car-repair bills, and in this case the

225

possibility of sneaking home at the interval, leaving David to do his worst with the Chanat.

And yet, orchestras are superficially grand. I watched the automatic busy-work of the players, the bow tightening, valve oiling, timpani tuning, slide spritzing and reed sucking that takes place hundreds of times every day all over the world. From West End pit orchestras to prep-school concert bands to village pickup groups, in every country on earth, strings are stretched, and tuned across guitars, fiddles, hollowed-out vegetables, all for the sake of *resonance*. With so many working so hard, with so much music escaping into the atmosphere, one must conclude that something quite worthwhile and desirable is going on. And when dozens of sombre-looking experts assemble on a vast stage, carrying diverse instruments of some antiquity and refinement; when their intention is to perform a work by a composer who somehow managed to stand out in a crowd now vanished for more than one hundred years; and when they are to be accompanied by a young pianist who is assumed to have spent twenty years preparing for this moment, then a certain amount of awe and anticipation are in order.

I forced myself into such a mood by pretending I was Chanat. I pretended that I was caught up in the creative swirl of his day, that what we were about to see was fresh, challenging and surprising. I pretended European music had not died.

You and David emerged from the shadows and walked to the front of the stage. David's hands were visibly red from having been soaked in hot water. You wore immaculate white tie and tails. So did David. Your face transmitted a frequency of doom, and greeted generous applause with a squint of pain. You held out a hand to usher David to the piano. When you looked at him you discovered, with noticeable shock, that David was smiling.

David's grin was electric enough in private, and I was heartened for his sake to see that it carried to the back of the hall like a Falstaffian guffaw. I may have been the only one to notice your glare of disapproval: others must have

226

mistaken it for further anguished preparation for the sombre work awaiting you on the conductor's platform. David stood and smiled out at us for just long enough that I thought you might bodily drag him to his seat. With a half-wink and a long-limbed skip, David avoided your guiding hand and took his place; in four or five funereal paces, you took yours.

Stomach-turning coughs and throat-clearings filled the hall. I began to ache for a cigarette. Mary exhaled slowly and stared at her hands in her lap. David, meanwhile, smiled blasphemously from the stage, at the controls of his gigantic black music machine. It was fascinating to watch how hard your face had to work to convey to David that you wanted him to sober up, without betraying your meaning to audience or orchestra. I love to think that you believed David was literally drunk at the keyboard, performing while intoxicated. If so, you must have thought your comeback would last no longer than one horribly deformed first movement.

I must introduce one more personal note, to say just how moved I was to stand at last on the same stage with David. After all the years of struggle, made up of the combined joy and anguish that is the artist's life, it was a humbling experience to look down the length of my baton and see his eager face staring up at me. It was not so different from the face I had first laid eyes on nearly twenty years before in the gloom of his parents' drawing room. At times like those a man has no regrets . . .

Unlike your French-horn player, who fluffed her entrance and caused a hall full of Brahms fans to wince in unison. On that ragged note, yet another rendition of the Second Piano Concerto was born, precisely one-hundred years after its conception.

Either David had over-reacted to my advice, or this was his natural inclination on the stage, for he smiled throughout the slow beginning and, unless I am quite mistaken, even

227

laughed out loud just before crashing into his statement of the first theme. He was as splendid to watch as he was to hear. This was a David Debrizzi neither of us had ever seen. He had achieved the musician's highest aim, which was to transcend his instrument intellectually and physically, to project character and personality, and to imprint upon a master's notes the stamp of individuality.

I, for one, wanted more. I wanted David to stand up and walk around the orchestra during his rests, to visit Barbara stage left, to inspect the dull-sounding timpani at the back, to tickle the concert master under his bowing arm, to give the forlorn French-horn player a forgiving hug. We were there to enjoy ourselves, and to my way of thinking the gorgeous tug of the music was only the background to our potential delight.

While David did not go so far as to leave his piano, he did loosen his tie – a small gesture, but a step in the right direction. No one in the audience disapproved. On the contrary, we all loved it. It says a lot about the staid world of our beloved music that a soloist's unbuttoning his collar in the middle of a concerto is newsworthy: not a single critic failed to mention it in the next morning's papers. Some would express moderate support for David's anarchic stunt; others would pour scorn on his penchant for showmanship.

Barbara's cello playing had, it seemed to me, profited from her intimate consultation with the pianist. Her mournful solo in the third movement sang out to us not, I am relieved to tell you, like visions of concentration camps, but like a good old romantic breeze through lakeside treetops, as was undoubtedly intended.

I ought to say that when it came to your conducting I never once felt that awful who's-leading-whom tension between any of the tripartite forces of your ensemble. Your expression may have been dour as drizzle, and your swooping, mosquito-like baton jabs may have looked a mite effeminate, but the whole thing rolled along nicely and I believe you brought the best out of your performers. The critics would certainly have taken this view, had they mentioned you at all, but then they would not have understood your grimaced warnings to David to wipe that smile off his face *or else*. The elegiac third movement was no place for grinning, in your book, and you tried to compensate for David's smile by practically turning around to face the audience so that we could see from your expression just exactly how grim the music was supposed to be. The best you could hope for, at that point, was that critics in the audience would take David's unusual manner for an indication of eccentricity – and therefore genius – or reliance on chemical stimulants. It was neither of these, of course. It was David living up to his promise to be joyful, an honest display of an interpreter's musical delight and professional relief. If you doubted that, then you doubted David's consummate mastery of the piano.

Brahms's almost reluctant 'big finish' exploded overhead as intended. There was applause. Do you remember the applause? What did you make of that applause? It wasn't exactly *huge*, you will have to admit. No one stood, no one fainted, only a handful of extroverted people shouted 'Bravo!'. Your disappointment was palpable, but somehow you managed to milk the applause so that it lasted through three complete orchestral standings up and sittings back down again. The obligatory conductor/soloist overhead handclasp, like a boxing referee announcing the victor, did not seem completely out of place. You did everything in your power to ensure that most people believed we had not witnessed merely another in a long line of perfectly good renditions of a pleasant piece of music.

Which was, I am afraid, the case – and that is why we have Chanat. After the one-drink and two-cigarette interval, we returned to the hall to find the stage cleared of everything but David's piano. We could sense at once that this was the reason most of the punters had paid for their seats: with due respect to you and your Brahms, they had come to hear Chanat.

David emerged from the wings still wearing his terrifically handsome smile, which was so infectious that we all smiled back at him as we applauded his entrance. 'Just watch *this*,' his smile said, which is exactly the spirit in which Chanat had composed the *Death Spiral*. David took his slow stroll around the circumference of the piano, sat down with a playful tail-flick, wrapped his left ankle around the leg of his seat, and hurtled into the opening of the Chanat with even more daring and exuberance than he had displayed on his – on *our* – recording.

This was great fun. The audience was propelled along by the frenzy of Chanat's mad composition. We felt like passengers trapped in a bus driven too fast along an alpine road by a suicidal drunk. This is the pianist I wish your readers had been told about, the alert, super-confident, devil-may-care David, who brought the music – and his audience – to the brink of collapse, to the edge of the alpine cliff, and steered them back to safety every time.

This was the David Debrizzi neither of us had seen before, and could never have predicted. He relished the stage. He was fuelled by the audience's every gasp, and gave off a rare and inspiring feeling of communal endeavour: we were all in this together; we were going to get through the *Death Spiral*, even if it killed us, and we were going to smile all the way.

The finale, the part I had played on David's album, was like a great exhalation – not so much sexual as epiphanic, or simply *athletic*. It was glorious. The audience, who had probably dozed politely through hours of humdrum ivory-tickling in this same hall, shot out of their seats and roared – *roared*, Geoffrey, do you remember? People looked at one another as they applauded, red-faced and disbelieving. One man near the front turned to the fellow standing on his left and clapped him triumphantly on the back, a gesture symbolic of what we all felt, which was that without our help David could never have pulled it off.

David bowed and smiled and waved, then left the stage to prepare for what would prove to be an even dozen curtain-calls. Something happened that I had never seen before, which was that the audience beseeched him to play an encore, then recognized by David's expression that nothing he could play now would improve on our musical feast, so that they actually began to applaud his decision *not* to play

230

an encore. I like to think that the applause was loud enough to cross the Channel and seep into the tomb Chanat shared with his sister Edwige in Montpellier.

Mary and I smoked a cigarette in the lobby before going backstage. This must have taken less than ten minutes, plus four or five minutes trying to convince an official that we were more central to David's entourage than the album-clutching fans gathered at the stage door. I imagined that during those minutes David would have taken off his jacket, washed his face, accepted your congratulations and those of the orchestral musicians who had bothered to stick around, and generally put his feet up after a job well done. I anticipated an important moment in his dressing room, one of those unspoken acknowledgements of life's actually being worthwhile on occasion. We would nod knowingly to each other, that is what David and I would do.

As Mary and I rounded a corner into the corridor where we knew David's dressing room to be, we were startled by the sound of a slamming door. At the far end of the corridor we saw your gangly figure emerge from a small pack of well-wishers gathered in wait for David. You strode angrily away from them, towards us, your tails flapping behind you, your precious baton case clutched under one arm. I would not have been unduly surprised if you had swept by me without a greeting, had I been alone; but Mary was your wife, after all, and we were astonished to see that you simply pushed between and past us without so much as a muttered oath.

'Goodness,' said Mary. 'Isn't *that* odd. I ought to go after him.'

I was too alarmed by your behaviour to comment, and merely kissed Mary goodbye before rushing down the corridor to David's room. Igor Malechievich, of all people, guarded the door, explaining to everyone that his virtuoso colleague did not wish to be disturbed. He placated them by signing an autograph or two himself. When he saw me he waved me to the door and, after a terse hello in French, let me inside.

231

David sat in the far corner of the room, in his shirtsleeves, with his arm outstretched on the backs of two chairs, like an exhausted boxer resting on his corner ropes. His face was flushed, but his eyes were dry and his mouth was set in an expression of rage that reminded me of his unsportsmanlike reaction to losing at chess. He did not look directly at me, but nodded in the direction of one of the chairs next to him. This was certainly not the important moment I had anticipated.

'Don't say anything,' said David, as I opened my mouth and uttered the first syllable of what was going to be a banal but heartfelt 'Congratulations'. I sat down and waited.

'Let me tell you something,' he said. 'Let me tell you what Geoffrey just said to me. I just *cannot* believe that man, sometimes. That idiotic, that ridiculous, that . . . that *fucking* Geoffrey *fucking* Flynch.'

I was all ears.

'May I have a glass of water, please?' he asked. 'And a cigarette? They're in my jacket pocket.'

He collected himself while I fetched his water and cigarettes. His jacket was still warm and damp. I sat down again and waited for him to sip his water and light his cigarette. His mouth twitched and his hands shook.

'I finished. I came back here. I felt very good indeed, thank you very, very much. It was all brand new for me, but still, somehow, familiar. I was conscious of . . . I was *conscious*, throughout, and I think you know what I mean. The performance and the reaction were there in front of me. They existed in advance.'

'I understand.'

'I came back here and he was waiting for me. Sitting right here. Are you ready for this, Pierre? He stood up and he said, "David Debrizzi," he said, "I am *ashamed* of you."'

'No.'

'Yes. I thought he was joking, so I laughed. "Look at you," he said, in a way that made me stop laughing. "Look at you. You are a *clown*. Is that what you want to be? A *clown*?" I sat down. He wasn't kidding. He lectured me for ten minutes about my attitude, and how my attitude was going to change, and how I was going to learn some respect. Then he stormed out of here.'

'Look, David,' I said, thinking quickly. 'I know this is awful for you, but you just have to remember that the man is completely out of his mind. He is jealous. You upstaged him as no one has ever been upstaged before, right here on his home ground. You stole the show. He will apologize as soon as he realizes how foolishly and selfishly he has behaved.'

'That may be part of it, yes. But there's more. He thinks he knows *why* I let him down so badly. It's because—'

'Let me guess. You have been infected by a certain piano teacher. Am I right?'

'Exactly. You should have heard him. He was raving. "Him or me," he kept saying. "Him or me."'

'I still say he is jealous.'

'Do you know what he has in that stupid little case, other than his baton?'

'No.'

'My contract. Remember my contract?'

'I remember.' That was the piece of paper you had made him sign at your house in London.

'The "him or me" question is his to decide. He owns me.'

'Nobody *owns* you, David. No one can make you do anything.'

'He can make me play two-dozen more concerts, and he can make me play that *fucking* Brahms.'

'He can't.'

'He can.'

'Well, he can't make you stop smiling. Look, it was spectacular. Wait until he sees the reviews. Are you OK, David? You're shaking. Maybe we should—'

'Let's go somewhere and wait for the reviews. The way they do in show business. That's what this is, right? Show business?'

'You may have to greet your fans on the way out. Igor is keeping them at bay.'

'Igor's all right, isn't he.'

'Haven't I always said so?'

233

'We'll bring him along. And Barbara.'

'Fine.'

'And promise me one thing?'

'Sure.'

'That when this is over, I'll never have to play that *fucking* Chanat again either.'

'Done.'

David, Barbara, Igor, Igor's new girlfriend and I holed up in one of Igor's clubs. David's adrenalin and anger combined to make him a most entertaining drinking companion. Igor, who claimed to be on a two-month break from the piano, had grown up into a most charming and level-headed young man. He still drank cranberry juice for effect, but spiked it generously with champagne. He seemed genuinely to admire David, and to feel almost as protectively towards him as I did. It was Igor who stole out into the small hours to buy newspapers.

'Oh, no,' said David, when he had scanned two or three reviews. 'Geoffrey isn't going to like this much.'

The reviews mentioned you, but only in the same way they mentioned the venue and date of the concert. They mentioned the Brahms only by name, and by way of introducing the highlight of the evening. They mentioned David's tie-unbuttoning and smiling – this is where some of the scorn-pouring came in – and, as you will remember if you were able to read them through your blind rage, they called it a concert début unlikely to be rivalled in a decade.

'That's it, then,' said David. 'I suppose I am a real pianist now.'

'One bit of advice,' said Igor, unsteadily raising his glass. He seemed much older than David, and possessed an authority derived from his endless professional touring.

'Go ahead,' said David. 'I can take it.'

'Just keep smiling,' said Igor, who *never* smiled on stage.

Your

CHAPTER ELEVEN

▐▌▐▐▌

That was David's 'breakdown'? A little joy, a little smiling, perhaps a modicum of showmanship? *That* was David's '*breakdown*'?

That our first London concert was a fantastic critical success is a matter of historical record. But what the audience and reviewers detected – and chalked up to the eccentricity that is not unknown to our craft – was David's eerily distracted manner at the piano. It was as if David were thinking pleasant, far-off thoughts while the rest of us were focused on the music. As gratified as I may have been by the public's response to our performance, I was seriously concerned that David had begun to show signs of psychological imbalance. I considered cancelling the remainder of what I knew would be a gruelling tour. I thought again, though, and decided instead to try to excise the most stressful factor acting on David at the time: La Valoise had to go, once and for all. It did not take a trained psychologist to see what was at the root of David's problems. One look at the way he seemed to flinch or twitch whenever La

Valoise entered a room, and one look at his bizarre
performing style that was informed, I was certain, by
La Valoise's cavalier approach to life and music, and I
knew that without swift intervention David's career –
if not his mental health – was in serious jeopardy.

This is no mere distortion of facts, among countless others in your book; this is a bald lie. A more convincing 'breakdown' came months later. David had always shown little signs of strain – haven't we all? You could have pointed to these, and exaggerated them in your sledgehammer style, if you wanted to persuade people that you knew David was nearing emotional collapse. If you were honest you would have admitted that neither of us had a clue about how tortured David was inside. To us his first big performance was a victory, a summing-up, a release after so many years of hard labour. We forgot to think what it must have felt like for him, whose labour it actually was. It was as if David's long musical journey had come at last to a mountain pass, that he gazed out over the long-sought vista and was not exactly thrilled with what he saw.

Hindsight is the biographer's precision lathe. He uses it to hone a life into comprehensible form, into rational lines and smooth transitions. He trusts so much in cause and effect that he has no qualms about working backwards from what might very well have been fortuitous clashes of events. He wants to believe that any outcome has its roots in the subject's life. In this way a biographer might write that Chanat, as a child staring out of his bedroom window at a blighted vineyard, had put his suicide in train.

All we really know is that on stage, for the rest of your London concerts, David's performances were soulless imitations of the opening night. You had scared the wits out of him, and no amount of reassurance from me, or from Igor, or from Barbara, could help to rebuild the magical personality you had gone out of your way to suppress. You had made it perfectly clear that my staying away from the concert hall was not enough, that you wanted me out of the country. I clung to

236

the shadows, and did not realize the seriousness of your intent until I received a personal visit, at my hotel, from a sinister squad of solicitors claiming to represent you and David. Like everyone I detest lawyers, and your little band of trouble-makers were particularly loathsome in their style of dress and coiffure, and in their choice of euphemistic threats.

Precisely what you hoped to accomplish by sending in the troops, I have no idea. They could not prevent me from moving freely about the city. They explained to me that I had no legal right to profit from David's concerts, which was not news to me, and went on to compare my situation with that of an estranged husband seeking visitation rights to his child. I asked them please to shove off, and quickly called David to settle the matter once and for all.

'I suppose,' he said, sounding weak and exasperated, 'that if you left it would simplify matters. Just go.'

I went, wondering how much of this contretemps was due to your suspicion that your wife and I might have become too well acquainted. For clarity's sake I am going to abandon my little game and tell you the precise truth about my dealings with Mary. Are you sitting down? No, no, I am still only teasing you. You will find this difficult to believe – what with your tortured relationships with women stretching way back to the dark, virginal times before I introduced you to Anita and Gabrielle – but Mary and I spent those days gossiping like housewives and never, not once, did it occur to either of us that we might be on the verge of physical contact. Our relationship was built on the foundation of nicotine addiction and a common desire to giggle at your expense. It may surprise you to learn that for the past eight years Mary and I have conducted a secret correspondence of an entirely platonic nature. She is unfailingly loyal to you, even if she sometimes relates an unflattering anecdote about your – oh, let's call it what it is – your breathtaking *vanity*.

I retreated to Paris and my humble routine, certain that you would set about polluting David with anti-Pierre propaganda, turning him against me with your vile and calculating lies. I celebrated my fortieth birthday at the Père et Fils squeezing the breath out of a reliably incompetent chess opponent. I admit it, I moped. For a long time I had looked to my fortieth birthday as the time I would begin a programme of self-improvement – a bargain I had made with myself to justify years of unhealthy over-indulgence. I awoke the day after my birthday and threw myself into over-indulgence as never before, having quickly decided that fifty was a more sensible watershed age to make alterations in my way of life with a view to longevity.

I passed some time putting a large amount of my brother's money into a friend's restaurant, a project that has since proved wildly profitable – for my brother. I was so lonely and blue that I married a childhood friend whom I had always adored, and who was unlucky enough to have been widowed at thirty-nine. You have never met Françoise. She is most cheerful and cultured, and at the time she raised my spirits considerably. She ran a boutique right around the corner from my house, so that we were able to see each other off and on during the day. At night she wolfed down my cooking and afterwards requested that I play the piano for her. Now that I think of it, I believe I am still legally married to Françoise, although she moved permanently to Aix-en-Provence some time ago.

I paid a visit to David's parents, to boast to them of their son's success in London, and to translate the reviews for them. David's grandmother, Greta, listened in silence as I read out the notices in French. When I finished, she announced that she found it vulgar that David should be talked about in the newspapers. Her taste in music was surprisingly modern, and she complained that Brahms was 'just another antique German'. I replied that if she had been born to Viennese society rather than to Corsican peasantry, she might have *met* Brahms, who died when Greta was six years old.

Henri and Camille seemed oddly out of touch with their son. Of course they were proud of him, but they continued to worry that there might not be a secure future in the life David had apparently chosen, and that he was still easily young enough to train in a more conventional field. I said that I thought they were quite right in believing that David could adopt a new career at the drop of a hat, but that they ought to see him perform in Paris in a few weeks' time before telling him to do so. Henri, I am afraid, had sunk during his retirement into a sad state of alcoholic stupor – the slow, non-violent, French variety of the syndrome. He had grown plump and weepy. Camille, on the other hand, had never looked more robust. She and her aged mother-in-law were clearly holding down the fort together, and shared little jokes that Henri did not even pretend to understand. They both wanted to know how David had looked on stage. When I started to describe his posture and smile, they said 'No no, what did he *wear*?'

They loved David so much. If your nasty book is ever translated into French I will have to borrow enough money from my brother to buy every copy and have them all destroyed. Unlike me, and even less like you, they had always seen David as a complete human being. To me he had been a musical being first, from the very beginning. It had taken me years to separate the man from his fingers. I was glad to have paid my respects to David's parents, which put our recent triumphs and differences in perspective.

Your tour continued. You led a musical caravan around Europe – Amsterdam, Bern, Munich, Barcelona, Milan. David's performances were met with predictable acclaim, but I could not help thinking, as the notices trickled in, that the biggest winner in this enterprise was not you, and not David, but Chanat. Music, after all, was supposed to be central to the exercise. Chanat's other, even lesser-known works, began to crop up here and there on pianists' programmes from Oslo to Seattle. I know this because, as the world's acknowledged expert on the composer, I was sent Chanat-related materials from musicians all around the world. The *Death Spiral* was performed by no one else during this period, not because pianists were necessarily intimidated by David's rendition, but because they were all home furiously practising it and wondering how it could ever be played. Reckless critics in

239

the United States, where David's album had begun to catch on in a small way, speculated that his amazing recording had been achieved through technical treachery, which I secretly took as a compliment. They would see soon enough, if you had your way and David travelled to America.

It was during David's concerts in Munich that a last straw of sorts was delivered to me by a watchful German friend. This was the newspaper interview in which I was identified by name as David's 'long-time teacher', and described as a 'threat' to the pianist's career prospects. Ostensibly an interview with David, the piece carried the unmistakable stamp of your interference. I was said to have been 'dropped from the tour', as if David were a rock band and I a drug-addled drummer. The journalist, to whose newspaper I had contributed a nugget or two over the years, did not put these words into your mouth, but I have no doubt that you provided them. David's remarks were centred strictly on the music, especially the *Death Spiral* – and besides, David would never have thought, much less publicly stated, such cruel and baseless things about me.

Yes, I stamped my feet and pulled my hair and made my brand-new wife worry deeply about me. I took the article to German-speaking friends and asked them to tell me if I had lost my mind, or if I had been badly maligned if not libelled. I considered – then reconsidered – tracking you down and calling you up and issuing my long-desired challenge to a duel. I damned you to hell and invented new ways of calling down ill-fate upon a fellow human being.

I felt cheated and betrayed, trampled and abused, left-out and unloved. When Françoise was out of the house I played my own maniacal version of the *Death Spiral* at ear-splitting volume as a musical offering to the cruellest active gods.

I awaited your return for the Paris concerts in a state of livid, vengeful ire. I never heard from David; in my residual pride I wondered if your policy had been to intercept his mail. I collected notices and reviews and pored over them for clues to your behind-the-scenes activities. The occasional newspaper or magazine photograph trickled in, and I detected a steady deterioration in David's appearance. The reviews became steadily more negative – more so than could be accounted for by the inevitable backlash encountered by newcomers who make an initial splash. While they were never quite critical of David's playing, they began to suggest that his apparently limited repertoire betrayed a less than universal mastery of the instrument. I would have said that it was *your* repertoire that was limited.

David returned to Paris in mid-December. I waited for him to call me, which took roughly long enough for him to kiss Henri and Camille and Greta twice each, and to race to the telephone. We met that evening at the Père et Fils. He thrashed me at chess while telling me of his adventures. He talked and talked about the audiences, about the quality of the pianos provided for him, about the hotels, about your obsessive insistence on decorum at all times, about the girl or two he had spent nights with, about different kinds of food, about his horrendous lapse in concentration during the *Death Spiral* in Barcelona ('Nobody noticed, not even Geoffrey').

David's long and excited monologue gave me time to think of ways of not mentioning that he looked simply terrible, that his personality seemed to have undergone a transformation, that I was frankly alarmed by his nervous, wide-eyed demeanour. He looked gaunt, even jaundiced, and his normally relaxed chain-smoking was now jerky and manic.

'America is next, you know,' he said, waving his cigarette over a half-eaten plate of charcuterie. 'That's what Geoffrey says. Secret negotiations. Monolithic recording companies. Makes Profundo look like small beer, right?' Small beer? A Geoffreyism if ever there was one. 'Geoffrey has been back in London for a few days. He's looking at other ideas. The Chanat revival is a hit.'

'I've heard what Geoffrey is up to.'

You were exploring television avenues and, oddly, touting free-market entrepreneurship at every turn.

'David,' I said. 'You don't look well. Have you not been sleeping properly?'

He gave me a scolded schoolboy look. 'Please,' he said, patting his pockets for another cigarette pack. He found one, extracted a cigarette, ignited the tip with crossed eyes and a shaky lighter, and smoked it halfway down before passing out in his plate of meat.

'Nervous exhaustion,' said the doctors. 'That's all it is.'

With five days to go before the first Paris concert, there was some cause for concern.

David seemed more embarrassed than seriously ill. He spent three nights in hospital, although more than one was not strictly necessary. He rolled his eyes in wonder at the flowers and get-well telegrams that arrived from his many admirers. You cancelled important engagements to fly in to Paris, set up shop at the Hôtel de la Victoire, and milked David's predicament for all it was worth. You treated me with condescension and disdain. When and if my calls were put through, you spoke in an even haughtier tone than usual; an eavesdropper would have thought I was one of David's groupies hoping to insinuate myself into your circle in order to rub elbows with a star.

'Yes . . . ah . . . look here, La . . . ah . . . Valoise,' you said, after I had asked you just what the hell you had done to David during the past ten weeks. 'You might . . . ah . . . really try to show a bit of . . . er . . . restraint . . . ' The frequent hesitations endemic to your accent had crept up the scale of affectation, even at your advanced age, until listening to you speak was like watching someone about to sneeze. 'You are . . . ah . . . perfectly . . . ah . . . welcome . . . to . . . ah . . . pay the lad a visit. I *am* sorry. *Must* put down the . . . ah . . . phone. *Awfully* busy.'

It was thrilling, really, to be granted permission to visit David, when of course it was I who had driven him to the hospital in the first place. Poor Françoise, married to me only a matter of weeks, must have been somewhat disturbed by the way I danced around the house, chanting obscenities, clutching a bust of Liszt and pretending it was a voodoo doll in your image.

'Artists,' she said, when I had calmed down and come to bed. 'I knew it was going to be like this. He is only

242

pretending to be ill, am I right? That is the way they all behave.'

'Not David. You'll have to meet him. David is different. He has a sense of humour.'

'I have heard the way he plays. That Chanat? I am afraid your David Debrizzi *has* to be crazy.'

I nearly broke down and told her that the craziest parts of that recording were mine, but I still believed that it was my secret to keep for all eternity. Still, I don't want you to flatter yourself into believing that you are the first to know: there was someone else.

David moved back into his small flat for the first time in three months. He looked tired, and he did not feel up to practising even as his homecoming concert loomed, so I hesitated to pry too deeply into what had gone wrong during your tour of Europe. I spoke to him on the telephone and waited for him to broach the subject in his own good time.

'I hate making a spectacle of myself,' he said, on the day before the concert. We had met for lunch at the Epinard, home of a most interesting Roquefort-and-puréed-spinach dish, and David felt up to drinking white wine.

'Nonsense. Everyone knows how tiring a tour can be. Hotels, rehearsals, showing up on time, orchestral disagreements. No one likes to be pushed. And playing the *Death Spiral* – what, two dozen times?'

'Yes. Still, that's what I'm supposed to be good at. That's my job. If I don't play it no one else will.'

'Now what about tomorrow? You wouldn't be the first soloist to cancel. I don't want you to think you have to perform if you don't feel like it. You've been away from the piano for several days.'

'I feel fine. I want to be known as the pianist who *never* cancels.'

Something in the way David said this triggered my Geoffrey Flynch radar. I guessed that you had been pep-talking him again since his return.

'I wouldn't do it if I were you. It never hurts to be cautious.'

'I was cautious for long enough, frankly. When this is over I will have enough money to buy a little car, I think.'

'Was it ... was it *horrible* on the road?' I wanted to approach his difficulties as gingerly as possible. 'What I mean is, did you find that Geoffrey was at all hard on you? The way he acted in London scared us all.'

'Geoffrey? Was it? I just don't know any longer.'

'What I'm trying to get at is this,' I said, ginger no more. 'You left London in fine fettle. I kept up with your progress through the press. Everything seemed to be going fine. Then you returned something of a wreck, if you'll forgive my saying so. I thought you might fill me in.' There was a hostility in David's eyes that took me by surprise. 'If it's any of my business, that is.'

David wiped his mouth with a napkin and reached for his pack of cigarettes. 'I'm not exactly certain that it is. Any of your business.'

'Oh, well, fine, then.' It was time for me to reach for a cigarette of my own. We smoked and looked away from each other for a minute or two.

'I don't mind telling you a couple of things,' David finally said. 'One thing in particular, anyway.'

'Not if you don't want to,' I said.

I had never thought of David as a particularly fragile man, and it was disarming to see that he trembled slightly as he thought about how to tell me what he wanted to say. The disjointed monologue that followed was perhaps one hour long, and it will give you some indication of how I was affected by his words when I tell you that I did not speak at all during that time, and moved only to attend to my almost constant smoking.

David started by explaining that he thought it was about time he had his say, that he had been listening too long to the conflicting demands and petty bickering of his advisers. Someone in his position, he said, could only operate on the basis of trust. There was no way to rehearse a musical life,

244

he said – one had to play along and hope for the best. For twenty years he had done as he was told, practised hard, believed in you and me and our best intentions. All of the biggest decisions in his career – not attending a conservatoire; eschewing all competitions except for the Gaston-Robert; recording a work by an obscure composer before a proper début – were necessarily made for him, and he had taken their wisdom on faith.

It struck me that I had never before heard David talk about himself or his feelings. I would never have said that it was in his makeup to look back, to court regret, or to dream of complaining about his lot in life. Even now it seemed to require great effort on his part to bring up the past. He spoke slowly, not so much because he wanted to choose his words carefully, but because he had only just begun to sort out what he wanted to say.

He started out diplomatically enough, where you were concerned, saying that he had been wary of you as a foreigner, as a vaguely threatening figure from the musical establishment, as someone who seemed to pop into his life every now and then like an eccentric uncle home from dangerous expeditions. He had looked to me, he said, for day-to-day guidance at and away from the piano. All of this rang true for me, and I began to sense where he was going. I thought he was going to let off long-pent-up steam about the professional pressures you had put on him since you decided it was time for a European tour. I thought he was on the verge of asking me to act as intermediary so that he might be released from further obligation to you without having personally to enter into demeaning offstage battles.

Not a bit of it. He had only just begun. He described his guilty feeling of disloyalty in the months before he recorded his album, when he started to think that my approach was unprofessional and too *laissez-faire* for the competitive world of the professional musician. He said these fears had been entirely divorced from our friendship; in fact, he had worried that our closeness might turn out to be an impediment to the rational planning of his career. The piano was going to be

245

his *life*, after all, and in the end my example was not one he hoped to emulate.

This had troubled him for some time, but he had decided not to make waves. Everything had gone smoothly, if un-conventionally, until then; and anyway he had always had a special fondness for what I had to say about piano music. As he started to think more independently, in his early twenties, he found that he still agreed with my musical outlook in general. 'Most of all,' he told me, 'you could really *play*.' He liked having a hands-on teacher, like an officer who would never order his men to do something he wouldn't do himself. He felt that his trust in me had paid off, and saw no reason why he ought to make drastic changes in our arrangement.

Now David really struggled to put his words in order. I did not believe for a moment that his 'nervous exhaustion' was anything more serious than a need for rest after a stressful and intensive new experience, but it unnerved me to see my old friend fighting back any emotion that might prevent him from finishing his monologue.

He said he had been happiest during the months before we went to London to record the Chanat. He enjoyed the way we used to scoff at the music together, while still adoring the whole ecstatic mess of Chanat's life and creations. His confidence peaked just in time for the recording session. He liked being at the centre of attention. He liked seeing Igor again as an equal, and reminded me of our old joke about him: 'Malechievich? You mean the Russian defective?'

Then David's voice suddenly went cold. He gripped the edge of the table with one of his hands. He leaned forward.

'Everywhere I have been,' he said, 'there have been people who wanted to see me play, wanted to talk to me, wanted me to sign my name. Why? Because of my Chanat. That's all we heard out there, you know. The Chanat revival. The Chanat explosion. I had done something original, something amazing. Piano *aficionados* had been waiting for generations to latch on to a phenomenon like this – like me. And do you know what I thought for all that time? Do you?' He was not asking me to respond. 'At first I thought – that's right, look at me. Just *look* at me. Pierre was right – the *Death Spiral* was a miracle, and I would be called miraculous. But I had an awful feeling, like nausea. There was something wrong. I felt that I knew perfectly well what it was. That I had known all along but would not admit it to myself. And then I really *did* know.'

David leaned back from the table again and looked around the restaurant to check for eavesdroppers.

'Do you know how many times I have listened to my own recording, Pierre?' He shook his head for me. 'Once. One time. The night at Geoffrey's house with Igor and Boris and everyone else. That was the only time. Afterwards I never wanted to listen to it again, because I thought what I heard the first time might turn out to be true.'

I bowed my head and wished I could wake up elsewhere. I wanted to speak, but David's confession hung like a heavy curtain between us. I clung for a moment to his remark that he had only heard the recording once, then reminded myself that he had been trained to remember music in its every nuance at one hearing, and his powers exceeded even my prodigious ability to store notation and sound.

In a weak voice, David reminded me of our emotional day not so long ago, when a loss at chess had sent him over the edge. 'That was when I admitted to myself that the recording did not belong to me, and when I realized why you felt you had to interfere.'

I wanted to say that it had been a simple accident, a bungled engineering job, but when I opened my mouth to speak I was immediately silenced by David's raised hand.

'I was grateful, at first. There was so little time. I imagined the way you must have listened to my recording, after so much effort, and your disappointment when it did not live up to your expectations. You had to step in. You had to make it perfect.'

His interpretation of my motives was so far wide of the mark that at first I did not know quite what he meant. And then it dawned on me that there was some truth in what he said.

247

'I thought, That's it. I have trusted this man all my life. I thought he believed in me. I thought when he said "Good job", he *meant* it.'

David went on to accuse me of various sorts of treachery and deceit, as my mind raced to think of a convincing way to explain to him that something that appeared so calculating on the surface, was actually an honest mistake compounded by an ingenious solution. I thought there might even be humour in the story. Still, I could not find my voice, and with a shiver I glimpsed a part of me I had never hoped to see, an unconscious actor who had erased David's tape deliberately in order to have its own musical say. A monster.

'I never told Geoffrey,' David said, much to my relief. 'Or anyone else. I was too embarrassed. I was too ashamed.'

What about London? I wanted to ask. What about all the fun we had there, and the wild success of his first concert?

'And what about London the next time?' David said. 'By then . . . '

I won't write down his actual words, which were so cruel that I allowed a match to burn down between my fingers without noticing until I smelled my own burning flesh. The point was . . . the point was that by that time David had decided I was not really a part of the music 'business', that I was a bystander like any autograph-seeker or third violinist.

'Where are your other students?' he wanted to know. 'Why do you *laugh* at the music I have to play for a living?'

I stuck to my silence, and my growing anger, under succeeding waves of David's attack.

'Do me a favour,' he said. 'Don't bother coming to the show tomorrow night. Just don't bother. I'll do fine without you.'

He pushed back his chair and stood up, with one more glance around the room to make certain no one of any importance was within earshot.

'You're a liar, Pierre,' he said. 'And pathetic.'

Chanat was not an intellectual man. Like so many of his contemporaries, he strove only to live a life of perpetual artistic ecstasy. During the years of despair and poverty that he endured after his disgrace, he must have looked to his art for consolation. It was nothing like our era, when we scour the archives for idols; Chanat was surrounded by them, in the flesh. Just imagine the feeling of gazing out at the musical landscape with an eye to conquering it, and spying Wagner there.

Chanat tore up music as fast as he could write it down. There can be no doubt that Chanat's proficiency at improvisation meant that his greatest pianistic achievements evaporated into the thin air of his ante-electronic age. His surviving manuscripts betray an impatient hand. His output was extremely uneven, often relying solely on technical gimmicks. He must have been the most self-absorbed and lonely of men, for no one has admitted for posterity to being Chanat's friend.

Chanat had not yet given up hope. He planned to use the only weapon at his disposal – his piano technique – in order to force the world to recognize and revere him. He practised night and day on an inferior instrument, unaware that he had probably reached the limit of technique already. He could see only two ways forward: one was to alter the established piano itself to see if it were possible to play faster and louder; the other was to alter his hands in some way to achieve the same result. Lacking the knowledge and craftsmanship required for the former route, he resolved to attempt the latter. He went to work on his hands and fingers, stretching them and exercising them with strings and weights. He wrote in his diary of his desire to write and play a piece of music containing ten parallel melodies – not a fugue but a mêlée. He slept with his hands suspended by a traction device of his own invention. He consulted a masseuse, who must have been amused to be paid the going rate for sexual intercourse merely to knead his hands and wrists with oils and astringents. He worked his digits so hard that he boasted in writing that he could hang by each one of his fingers almost indefinitely, and spent many hours a day doing precisely that.

His diary does not say whether or not his playing improved, or if he felt any closer to a pianistic breakthrough that would make Liszt and the others sit up and take notice; in fact, the diary stops for three months towards the end of 1842, not because he had nothing to record, but because he had injured his writing hand so badly that he could not hold his quill. We can only infer that playing the piano was even more out of the question. The silence of Chanat's diary resonates with his self-inflicted misfortune. His shaky left-handed penmanship reappears to inform us that his self-inflicted injury was a *good* thing, that his character had been strengthened through pain and disappointment, that he had *increased* the weights on his pulley system and hoped to be playing again by Lent.

Needless to say, Chanat never performed again. He was able to compose at the piano, but he was never able properly to play the *Death Spiral* – a frustration that surely contributed to his miserably unsuccessful suicide attempt. As he writhed in pain on his death bed, Chanat must have achieved a glorious plane of romantic satisfaction at having failed so spectacularly both in life and in death.

At least Chanat failed spectacularly. I felt that I had failed ignominiously, cravenly. I thought I might never know to what extent you had prejudiced David against me. I had to assume, knowing that David was now an independent thinker, that he had arrived at his own conclusions. He no longer needed me – that much I could have understood; but now he considered me a pathetic liar, an unbalanced man who had deliberately sought private glory in the corruption of his work.

I retreated to the bosom of my new wife. I pretended to ignore the reviews of David's Paris concerts. I watched the Chanat revival ignite in my country and abroad without contributing comment or written word. I sat up late at night in my marble hall, drinking coffee and smoking cigarettes, glowering at my Bösendorfer. I had a mean-spirited affair with the sister of my brother's last wife but one. I opened the curtains and let in the light and played Mozart badly, on purpose. I marvelled at the shallowness of a man who could

250

pretend for twenty years that a single piano student – yes, I know: alter ego, replacement son; you have droned on about this enough yourself – could vicariously fulfill his musical ambitions. I felt hurt and meek. I felt old and wasted and cowardly. I was as ashamed of myself as David was.

I do not wish to imply that there were no ways at all in which La Valoise was of use to us over the years.

Here is Geoffrey at his most magnanimous.

I can still hear the way he played in my own home on those tranquil evenings at Dollsworthy, when La Valoise enlightened us all with his bountiful talent. Whatever inner turmoil had caused his public downfall, it must have informed his highly refined and emotive playing.

When I have finished writing to you I shall have to go inside to the piano and see if this is still true.

. . . and yet I cannot pretend that I was not greatly relieved when David made his final break with his teacher of so many years. His path seemed clear at last, and it pleased me that it was David himself who made the decision to remove the obstacle of the Frenchman's bizarre and confusing influence.

Thus do I depart from your increasingly arrogant and self-serving volume. David's *Life* is set to soar. If only I had followed in Chanat's footsteps and at least *tried* to kill myself, perhaps your readers would have felt slightly less let down at this point. If they have any pity, they will wonder what became of me.

It is understandable that you deprived your readers of the reason for David's decision, since you did not know it. I often wondered what your reaction would have been had David told you his version of my infamous meddling in his recording

251

of the *Death Spiral*. Your political instincts would probably
have taken over, and you would have demanded a cover-up.

As it was, you forged ahead and entered negotiations for
another recording deal. Why, you must have wondered, did
David balk at the idea? Why was he so adamant that he needed
more time before he recorded the Brahms – or anything else,
for that matter? You must have decided that David now
suffered from a paranoid fear of the recording studio, a
condition that must be unique in the musical world. There are
plenty of examples of instrumentalists who suffer more or less
severely from stage-fright, like me; to be afraid of the studio,
like David, was incomprehensible. Knowing the facts, one can
only speculate that David associated the recording experience
with trickery, and a kind of failure. He honestly believed
that I had erased and replayed his *Death Spiral* because his
version wasn't good enough, and because in my diabolical
way I wanted to immortalize my own performance. I can
only imagine the months of cajoling that you spent trying
to force David back in front of the microphones.

No Frenchman likes to think of a compatriot having
to stay in London for long. As reports trickled in about
David's having 'settled' in London, it pained me to imagine
the grotesque meals he would be required, out of politeness,
to swallow; the airless pubs he had exchanged for the Père et
Fils; the company of Englishmen; the sorry gloom of Britain.
This thought was almost as distressing as the idea that David
lived in a perpetual state of anger towards me. He never called,
he never wrote. I had to assume that I regularly crossed his
mind, and that each time he dismissed any thought of getting
in touch with me.

I know that I am giving you the impression that I was
obsessed with David. I tried not to be. Life went on. I had
a new wife to cook for. Françoise was a hard-working,
hard-living woman, and except for her incompetence at chess
she was an ideal companion. A born diplomat, she was the
first of my wives to be able to tolerate the other members
of my increasingly boorish family. She listened patiently to
my stories about David, and counselled retreat. She gently

proposed that I forget about him, and that I give some thought to gainful employment. The restaurant business, she said, was where I clearly belonged.

I tried to give Françoise's suggestion the amount of consideration that sound advice deserved. She was a businesswoman herself, after all – her boutique was prospering. I wrote mental menus and envisioned decor. I pictured a restaurant called La Valoise, with a chef poached from the Père et Fils, waiters recruited from my other favourite spots, and a *sommelier* I knew in Lyon who considered me a novice and would jump at the opportunity to be paid for edifying an old friend.

I spent perhaps two days toying with the idea, feeling the enthusiasm drain out of me. The restaurateur's calling is a high and noble one, but I found myself sneaking into my marble hall just to *look* at my piano, and I began to play it with a new fascination. It might be that in David's absence I had to rely on myself for adequate piano music. Françoise noticed that I had begun to play more seriously. She knew me well enough not to suggest out loud that I try to attempt a comeback, but she said it all with her eyebrows as she applauded my evening performances. Like everyone I was actually aware of having only one chance in life – one *take*, if you will – and decided to wage war on my former, self-pitying character.

I spent a year on that campaign, with no noticeable results. Françoise grew impatient with me, and threatened to move to a warmer climate. I was paralysed by an immature self-doubt. I had arrived at an age and time of life when most men look across the dinner table at their slobbering young children and decide that they ought to turn their attention to making them turn out well; or when they take stock of experiences and achievements with a view to building and broadening.

I will admit it: I was a cipher. Without the cachet of being David's teacher and discoverer, even music was no longer a source of pride. I began to think that I shared a certain number of characteristics with the unjustly maligned Leopold Mozart, having thrown in my lot with David and lived not for him but *through* him. I could not decide what made me

253

unhappier – David's rejection of me as a friend, or David's rejection of me as a mentor.

So that Françoise would not think I was insane, I collected my information about David in secret. A few loyal friends provided me with whatever fruit they could pluck from the musical grapevine, and thanks to your heavy-handed publicity there was no shortage of gossip and interviews in the British press. You had somehow succeeded in making the world believe that you had stumbled upon David in a French orphanage, then dedicated yourself to his musical education and general upbringing. 'See how well he speaks English?' you seemed to be saying. 'He has me to thank.' 'His amazing skill? The predictable result of living in the home of a man devoted to music and musicians.' All of this you were able to convey to your friends and the public at large without once abandoning that cloying self-deprecation, that paradoxically self-promoting 'Who, *me*?'

I heard, now and then, that David had visited Paris. He did not frequent restaurants where he knew he might run into me. He must simply have *burned* with hatred not to send some sort of conciliatory signal to me. My reaction was a cowardly one. I moped about antisocially, boring my acquaintances with dreary and fatalistic remarks about my failed life. Françoise, thinking that it might be a wife's place to chide her husband into productive activity, became more forceful in her criticisms of my laziness, my stubbornness, my irascibility, and my preoccupation with the past.

I continued to fume. A further year elapsed. The David I read about was not the David I had known. With his second recording scrapped, you led him to America. There he gained a reputation for cancelling concerts, falling dramatically ill, playing only the severest tests available when he managed to show up, and always finishing with the *Death Spiral*. What I could not begin to gauge was David's happiness. Had he not specifically asked me to guarantee that after his first tour he would never have to play that '*fucking*' Chanat again? Had he not been crushed when you said you were 'ashamed' of him? What could possibly have changed his outlook so totally?

The answer struck me, as answers tend to strike, in my morning bath. How clear it was, and how ridiculously I had behaved. The evidence, I thought, could not have been more conclusive: David dreaded the studio out of a sense of betrayal; he continued to play the *Death Spiral* in public in order to prove to himself that he was capable of doing so on his own; he did not contact me for the simple reason that he was the student, I was the teacher, and it was up to me to take the initiative; he fell ill and cancelled concerts because he was sad and he was wounded, and because he believed that he had been abandoned *by me*.

I remember springing out of my bath and racing to the bedroom to tell Françoise the news of my revelation. She said she was happy to hear it, and could I please go out to buy some bread. I dressed quickly, then burst into the sunshine feeling better than I had in ages. My neighbourhood glistened in a slanting autumn sun after a night of silent rain. All would now be fine. A gingerly approach – a formal message through David's parents, perhaps? – and David would be released from his despair. There would be a reunion full of meaning.

One thing was certain, I thought, as I marched down the steaming pavement, nodding good morning to my fellow early-risers: David had learned his lessons well. He knew about grace and humour. He knew about friendship and dedication. He knew the difference between a career and a vocation. My God, would we laugh about it all. We would shake our heads and grin at each other and slap each other's cheeks and call each other fools. I would cook a splendid dinner, Françoise would have the pleasure of meeting David, and I would toast my formal oath that David would never again be required to perform the Chanat.

I was so happy that I forgot about the bread. I dropped into the Père et Fils for the strongest of coffees and just the tiniest glass of red wine. I asked a new waiter to bring a chair and table outside so that I could smile at passers-by. I installed myself there and drank and smoked happily, content in my analysis of the situation, and confident that all would soon be resolved.

Perhaps I am telescoping events – we biographers do that, don't we, Geoffrey? But there was a morning, and there was coffee and wine and cigarettes, and there was my old friend Bertrand running up with a newspaper in his hand, asking a very silly question indeed. 'Have you heard?' he asked, absurdly. 'David Debrizzi is dead.'

Your

CHAPTER TWELVE

I snatched the newspaper from Bertrand's hand. It was folded to the pertinent item. David Debrizzi, the French concert pianist, had died in New York after collapsing backstage following a performance at Robinson Hall. He was twenty-eight years old. Bertrand looked searchingly at me, as if I had the authority to contradict the terrible news. I thanked him for bringing me the paper, and asked him please to leave me alone. When he had gone away I finished my wine and coffee. I stared at my shoes on the wet pavement. I studied a soaked cigarette end, waiting for a more suitable and instinctive reaction to set in. The three standard emotions, I told myself, would succeed one another during the next hours or days: disbelief; rage; sadness. I decided to marshal my intellectual side and hurry the progression along.

'I don't believe it,' I said, aloud. That took care of the first response. I looked back at the newspaper item, a mere column-inch of last-second news.

'I am angry,' I said, slamming two ten-franc coins on the table and standing up.

That left only sadness.

I experienced an unaccustomed clarity of thought as I walked slowly away from the Père et Fils. The disappearance of friends, which I had weathered before, can be troubling; the death of David Debrizzi meant more than that, and would demand an almost humiliating level of public and private mourning.

My fellow Parisians, late and bothered, hurried past me. I moved so slowly that I was able to look carefully at the faces of those walking towards me. They looked younger than the Parisians I had noticed the last time I had made the effort, which could only mean that I was older. Anyone who has suffered a serious blow knows the sensation of milling amongst oblivious strangers, feeling that somehow they ought to *know* one's private grief. And yet they pressed on, and so did I.

My view today is so obscured by your published version of events that I am scarcely able to remember the vivid catalogue of memories I summoned up during my short walk home. It would have been natural enough for me to think, 'Geoffrey killed him.' I could have settled on that convenient alibi. Perhaps I did think it, for the briefest moment. And yet I can say, in all honesty, that my thoughts ran instead through an orderly series of vignettes from my life with David, over a scrapbook of private images.

When David was a little boy, a perfect little boy, he used to squint at me sceptically over musical points of order. I remember his fingernails over the keys, clean, pink and white from pre-practice scrubbing and soaking. His hands stayed flat over the keys, solid and prepared, as he squinted at me. 'You know what I'm talking about,' I might have said. 'There is a sort of tockata-tockata-*shing* to that phrase. It's the *shing* I'm not hearing.' 'Like this?' he might ask, playing the phrase without looking away from me. '*Shing*? Like this?'

'Much better.' The piano teacher's catch phrase: '*Much* better.'

I walked past David's parents' house. Would they have heard the news by now? Would you have called them? Did you consider yourself David's chaperone? What, exactly, *were* your responsibilities? I picked up my pace and moved on.

I stopped at the storefront of Taubin's, the piano dealer. He had moved to my neighbourhood from the 17th *arrondissement* three years before. I looked in the window at the pianos – many of Igor's second-rate Mishigos among them. I remembered the day I bought my piano in Taubin's old display room. I was fifteen years old. Monsieur Presteron and my father drove me there, and stood in the background as Taubin and I selected an instrument. I remember that my father kept looking at his pocket-watch while I tested one instrument after another. Monsieur Presteron tried to remind him that this was an important purchase. Taubin took my picture standing next to the Bösendorfer I selected, the same piano that dominates the main room of my house to this day. The piano David grew to love. The piano Virginie had nursed along through years of Chanat's indirect abuse.

I felt a tap on my shoulder. It was Taubin, who had arrived to open his store. He had a newspaper under one arm, and did not say hello as he unlocked the door. He locked it again behind us. Six months before, I had attended Taubin's seventy-fifth birthday party; he hadn't changed since the day I caught his eye and pointed decisively at the Bösendorfer at the front of his showroom. The pianos still looked the same, too. Driving enthusiasts must feel similar pangs of longing at antique-car dealerships. There were second-hand pianos fifty, sixty, seventy years old, buffed and internally rebuilt. There were pre-war Steinways gleaming like Hitler's staff cars. The uprights lined the walls like respectful sentinels.

Taubin went into his office without saying a word to me. I knew then that he had read the news in his paper. I prowled about the showroom, drawing an index finger along the curved edges of the concert grands, just as David used to do before a performance. It was so quiet in the showroom, and yet so much sound was so near at hand. There were enough pianos in that room to accommodate the ghosts of those responsible for nearly the whole of the piano repertoire. Chanat would have been consigned to one of the brown uprights at the back – but he would have made the best of it.

Taubin had lined one wall with photographs and other memorabilia. Pianists, conductors, singers, teachers, piano makers, politicians, philosophers, poets and actors – all were represented by image or certificate of sale. There were hundreds of photographs, most of them autographed. A connoisseur would have been able to identify every one of the pianists. They were arranged chronologically by date of birth. Some of the better-known personalities had been enlarged and ostentatiously framed: Taubin wanted to sell pianos, after all.

There were two pictures of me. The first, framed in silver, showed me at fifteen, standing beside my newly-bought Bösendorfer with Monsieur Presteron in the background; the second, framed in black, showed me alone with the same piano a year later, on stage at the Salle Thierry.

There were two pictures of David. The first, framed in black, showed him at eighteen, standing beside the Steinway I had helped him pick out – and that you paid for; the second, framed in gold, showed David alone, with a different piano, on stage at the Salle Thierry.

Taubin emerged from his office with keys in his hand and a pipe in his mouth. He said he ought to open the doors. I asked him to wait a moment, and I sat down at his most prized piano: a Bösendorfer just like mine. I will not tell you what piece I played, but if you walked into a recital in London tonight there is a good chance you would hear it. Taubin stood near the door, sucking on his pipe. I finished the piece and softly shut the piano lid.

'Formidable,' said Taubin, unlocking the door to his shop.

'Wasn't it,' I said. I shoved my hands into my pockets and walked back outside.

The death of David Debrizzi had so far lasted twenty minutes.

I could still feel Taubin's Bösendorfer vibrating in my fingertips as I paused outside his showroom to light a cigarette. It occurred to me that I had been neglecting my own instrument, despite having played so much since my most recent marriage. I had not shown my noble old Bösendorfer the proper veneration. I remember that as a young man I used to bow to my instrument whenever I entered the room, whether I intended to play it or not. I missed my piano, and felt that I had a great deal of making up to do.

In the old days my dinner guests knew it was not done to ask me or David to play the piano; if I invited a chef to dinner I would never dream of asking him to prepare dessert. Whenever David attended one of my parties I could see my other guests glancing at the mute piano, hardly able to prevent themselves from begging one or both of us to play. I suppose my real objection was that my guests were not deserving, and were unable to reciprocate. I freely admit that this was a twisted view, and that the same rationale had coloured my professional advice to David. Not only did I believe that concert-halls full of coughing spectators could never fully appreciate what they heard and beheld, but I believed that the music itself was somehow unworthy. During the death of David Debrizzi I saw clearly how wrong I had been on that score. I thought how many hours – how many measures – of piano music had died with David, and I regretted every missed opportunity to have them heard.

Even now – right now, as I hurry to complete my letter before the welcome arrival of my visitor – I shudder with the realization that your *Life*, for all its solecisms, its personal attacks, its distortions and its self-serving lies, has managed correctly to depict at least one historical fact: I was misguided and miserable, self-absorbed and narrow-minded – in a word, *inert*. If David had not died for those forty-five minutes, I may very well have carried on in my obsessive, vengeful way, full of spite and envy. As it was, I made my way home to a slumbering wife, tip-toed into my marble hall, bowed to my Bösendorfer, and vowed to reclaim the instrument as my own.

*

The telephone rang. Without taking my eyes off the piano, walking backwards, I reached out with a dead hand and picked up the receiver.

'Hello, Pierre,' said David. I hadn't heard his voice in two years. 'Hello, Pierre,' he said. 'I'm in New York. I didn't want you to worry.'

'David. How nice to hear your voice. Why would I worry? Tell me all your news.'

> *I do not wish to discount the severity of David's 'illness', but there was one rather morbidly hilarious incident in New York, when a wire-service put out the mistaken news that David had collapsed after a performance and died en route to the hospital. There were so many ambulances that night, and so many New Yorkers dying, that I cannot say I am surprised that a mix-up occurred. There must have been quite a few startled fans out there, but I am happy to say that David was able to reach his parents before they read the dreadfully erroneous report. Mark Twain quotes were duly trotted out the next day.*

Your Chapter Twelve is surprisingly upbeat. You leave David recovered from his 'illness' and, though you once again call him 'reclusive', he is presumed to be happy. Your readers, most of whom will have bought your *Life* owing to the tantalizing mystery of David's disappearance from the concert stage, will have learned how hard you tried to convince David to emerge from 'hiding', if only to satisfy a lust for Chanat the world never knew it had. David and Chanat are linked like Siamese twins at the end of your narrative, as if they could not exist separately from one another, as if theirs were not distinct *Lives*.

> *Of course there were moments of worry. Specialists were consulted. They were in agreement that David's health was not in serious danger, but they could not agree on a specific malady to account for his collapse.*

Who knows what psychological forces act on the physi-
cal balance of an artist?

Who knows, indeed. Would it be too pedestrian to say that
David reacted adversely to overwork and stress? What a
surprise. It is a simple truth that 'artists' are allowed, and
often *encouraged*, to manifest the symptoms of exhaustion
or rage to which most people would love to give vent week
in and week out at their stifling jobs, but would be fired
for indulging.

David, if you will, had come up against the fearsome
wall of any artist's . . .

Nothing of the kind. It is always so simple to drop the
word 'artist' into a sentence to justify almost any theory
of psychological fraying, of moral ambiguity, of domestic
irresponsibility. Here you begin to erect your up-to-date
apology for David's apparently inexplicable retreat from the
stage, his deviation from the path you had fought so selflessly
to clear for him.

   You are wrong, of course. My prediction of so long ago
– that no man could withstand the strain of performing the
Death Spiral every night – had come true. Just look what
composing the piece had done to Chanat. David regained
his energy, took a good look around, and decided on a
course of action. All I can say is that Chanat could have
used a friend like David during the trials of his early
years in Paris.

David came home to Paris six weeks later. He was greeted
by a certain amount of public attention and speculation. As
a Frenchman, he was held in reverence – and some suspicion
– for having created a stir abroad. I wanted to surprise him
and to cheer him up, by meeting him on familiar ground. I
decided to pretend that our estrangement had never been. I
installed myself at the Père et Fils one hour in advance of
our arranged rendezvous. I tapped the face of my inherited

263

pocket-watch. When I saw David rounding the corner two blocks away, it really was as if he had never left.

I stood up to greet him, but remained behind the table. We shook hands, and David waved hello to our *patron* behind the bar.

'You look fine,' I said, as we sat down.

'I feel well enough,' he said. 'I don't enjoy flying much, though.'

'Have you been looking up old friends?'

'You are the first. My parents send their regards. They seem all right.'

'I'm glad.'

It was time to smoke and drink. It was a clear, pleasant evening, and I was proud of the women who walked by. David crossed his legs, leaned back in his chair, and sighed. I could see that he was happy to be back in the old routine. Our reconciliation would be swift and enjoyable.

'I hear you have a new wife,' he said.

'That's correct. She is French. Her name is Françoise.'

'Not a musician, I hope?'

'No. Françoise is a businesswoman. Very sensible and stylish. You'll like her.'

'I'm sure I will.'

David loosened his tie, tapped his cigarette on the rim of the ashtray, and smiled at something.

'What is it?'

'I was thinking I hadn't had a good game of chess in ages. We'll have to play soon.'

'I've got awfully good, you know. You won't stand a chance. No, it will be a humiliating massacre. A senseless loss of life.'

'Right.'

David's hair had grown quite long. I had seen photographs of him in New York, where his paleness was evident even in black and white. There had been a worrying vacancy in his eyes. Now a healthy colour had returned to his complexion, and his eyes glinted with calm good humour.

After our second drink David raised one of the many topics I thought he might have wished to avoid.

'Geoffrey is mad, you know,' he said. 'I wish you could have been there. He never slows down. He is consumed by worry at all times. He is terrified of putting a foot wrong. It's an impossible combination – relentless energy and constant fear. He's like a thief who feels sorry for the people he robs. Oh, and something else I've decided. Do you promise not to tell?'

'No.'

'I'll tell you anyway.'

'I thought you might.'

'Geoffrey is really not a very good conductor.'

I'm sorry, Geoffrey, truly I am, but this remark had us wheezing with laughter. David performed an uncannily accurate imitation of you – lips puckered and eyes huge with expectation and elbows pointing out sideways and baton raised like a fairy godmother's magic wand. 'People. *People*!' he mimicked. 'You simply *must* concentrate harder.'

'The poor man,' said David, when he could breathe again after laughing. 'Imagine being English.'

We were having a good time. We ordered food with extraordinary precision, for David had not eaten a proper meal in months, having been out of the country.

David asked me if I had heard about his failure to return to the recording studio. I confessed that I had followed his activities with a care bordering on fanaticism.

'It's a bit of a joke, really. Geoffrey wanted to conduct. I didn't have the heart to say that I wouldn't trust him to do a good job, so I just swooned a lot and said I was afraid. Who wants to record the Brahms, anyway? I've played it so often now I can't remember why I used to like it. You should have seen him when I said I was "afraid". Suddenly the whole world made sense to him. He had a dozen theories to explain my "studio-fright", as he called it – incompetent toilet training among them. Also acute awareness of mortality. Perfectionism. All very convenient for me, actually. I said "Yes, right, Geoffrey," twitching and shaking. "Just don't make me go back into that scary recording studio."'

We had drunk enough that I felt comfortable broaching the subject of my own anxiety about David's refusal to record again.

'I thought it was because of what I had done to your Chanat. I thought—'

'You're right. I really was very upset about that. For a long time. You'll have to admit, Pierre, that you could simply have *told* me. I could have played it again. I wanted to tell someone. Sue you. Recall the album. But then . . . '

'Yes?'

'But then I thought it was a nice secret to have. It is *our* Chanat, Pierre. You deserved a piece of it. It would only have confused people if we let on. In the end – you'll have to forgive me for saying this, Pierre. In the end I felt sorry for you.'

I had long since admitted to myself that my reasons for not telling David what I had done were complicated, and somewhat sinister. David had quite rightly punished me for stealing a part of what I had thought, in my deluded way, was rightfully mine.

'Now, David,' I said, in an exaggeratedly stern tone of voice. 'You didn't talk to me for months – for years. What was I supposed to think?'

'I could say the same thing.' David paused before continuing. He looked up and scratched his jaw. 'You, Pierre,' he said, smiling, 'are a challenging man.'

'H'm?'

'You used to complain that Geoffrey put all the pressure on me, that Geoffrey pushed me and risked . . . you know. Risked whatever it was we were all supposed to be working towards. Don't ask me what that is, by the way. But you were wrong. The real pressure, the real pushing, came from you.'

I put an innocent hand to my chest. 'From *me*?'

'You know exactly what I mean. You used to say that music wasn't a chess game, wasn't a boxing match? Well, music may not be, but I can now assure you that piano playing *is*. And guess who I was playing against?' David extended a well-trained index finger. 'Do you think I play as well as you do?'

'Silly question.'

'Is it? What would your answer be? Behind closed doors, man to man, who will play better?'

'Ah. Yes, well, *you* would win at chess. I take it all back about having improved. And at boxing too, for all I know.'

'And a piano duel to the death?'

'How very romantic of you.'

'Well?'

'Who would have won between Liszt and Chanat?'

'I'm asking about you and me.'

'A draw, David. A magnificent spectacle it would be, too. Let's call it a draw.'

I suppose it should have been obvious. Pulled this way and that, his career chosen for him at birth, as it were, David felt a need to stand back from his life and look at it from the perspective of adulthood. How many of us feel as if we have had a long career at the age of twenty-eight? One can honestly say that David literally retired.

'I have big plans,' said David, at the beginning of what you call his retirement. 'I was going to save this for later, but I can't wait to tell you. You are involved.'

'How nice.'

'I hope you won't disappoint me,' he said, back in his Geoffrey-voice. 'I want you to give a good account of yourself.'

'I'll give it my best, whatever it is.'

'Remember what I said, that you were . . . "pathetic", I think it was?'

'I remember, yes.' Was this going to be a grand apology?

'Well, I *meant* it.'

The rewards of the concert platform are plentiful and often glorious, but lionization is not everyone's cup of tea.

267

'Do you know how much I *hated* performing?' David asked me. 'There is only one reason to do it that I can see, and that is money. And money isn't a good enough reason to do anything. Not, at any rate,' here David rolled his eyes, 'when you are a *genius.*'

> *David Debrizzi is a genius, or rather he has genius.*
> *One can only hope that our loss is his gain, that he*
> *will have found some peace in isolation.*

'Here's what we're going to do,' said David. He took a folded piece of paper from his jacket pocket. 'You're going to love this, Pierre. I hope you haven't seen it before.' He flattened the piece of paper on the table and turned it around for my inspection. It was a photocopy of a letter, dated 5 January, 1847.

'That's Chanat's handwriting. No, I've never seen this letter before. Where on earth did you find it?'

'It was sent to me by an old woman in Montpellier. You're going to love this. She wrote to me and said she had "a box of Chanat's papers". Look here.' He pointed at the middle of the letter. 'Chanat alludes to his "Twenty-four Miniatures". My God, can you imagine a Chanat "miniature"?'

'And they really exist?'

'Pierre,' said David, tapping his fingers on the edge of the table, 'I *own* them. I swore the woman to secrecy. She believes I am the reincarnation of Chanat – you know the type. She delivers flowers to Chanat's and his sister's grave. She believes she is related to Chanat. When she heard my recording – *our* recording – she tied everything up with a purple ribbon and sent it all to me.'

'Have you played them?'

'I have.'

'And? How do they sound?'

'Well, "miniatures" they're not.'

'Naturally.'

'Each one is half an hour long at least.'

'Goodness.'

'They make the *Transcendental Etudes* look like *Für Elise*.'
'Good for Chanat.'
'Needless to say, they are outrageous and . . . '
'And ugly?'
'Ugly, yes. Sublimely so. There are several that probably cannot be played.'
'Not even by you?'
'Not even by *you*.'
'Wonderful. I can't wait to see them. They're complete? The manuscripts are original?'
'Original and complete.'
'I take it they're concert études? All keys?'
'That's right. To the extent that the initial key signatures ascend chromatically, major-minor. He doesn't stick to them, of course. You know Chanat . . . '
'I certainly do.'
'Recording them will be a momentous challenge.'
'Is that what you're going to do?'
David folded his arms. 'You don't understand at all, do you?'
'I suppose not.'
'Pierre. *You* are going to record them.'
'Oh, my.'
'Of course, those that seem to be for four hands . . . '
'Right.'
'And if you make any mistakes I may have to step in and—'
'Please.'
'It's going to drive your wife crazy.'
'My wife?'
'We're going to record them at your house. That room, and that piano, were *made* for Chanat. And so were you.'

One likes to think that David still plays the piano, that in his private world he reaches heights never before heard. I hope I have presented him fairly, as a young man who strove for perfection, who reached for the . . .

And so you dribble off into oblivion, out of touch and patronizing as ever. I suppose it did occur to you that David would actually *read* this blithering hagiography? Did you expect to flush him out into the open with your combination of bald flattery and needling disappointment? I can't wait to discuss it with him. Perhaps he will write you a letter of his own. In any case, the publicity generated by your book won't do our project any harm.

David lived on the royalties from his *Death Spiral* recording, which was reissued by a slightly more solvent company than Profundo. He was 'reclusive' only to the extent that he did not give interviews and he did not perform in public. He was photographed in the street, at the Père et Fils, entering the front door of my house. The media grew used to the idea that he had made up his mind never to perform again, and articles bemoaning this state of affairs appeared less and less frequently. Rumour took over from fact, and it was posited that David had suffered a nervous breakdown, that he had arthritis, stage fright, La Valoise Syndrome, failure of nerve, alcoholism, cancer. When his father died they predicted an Oedipal, or perhaps Mozartian crisis, and when this failed to materialize they focused on his relationship with his mother. Other women were blamed, too. His one recording sold as a testament to Chanat's glory and to David's evaporation. No one suspected that a mind-boggling project was under way – financed, I am happy to report, by my brother.

For two years we laboured and, yes, my wife had to move away. I will be accused of electronic trickery, of forging the scores, of usurping David's role as Chanat's rightful exponent, but the world will be amazed. My health may have suffered from all of this musical exertion, but my stay in the Alps seems to have put me right.

Much will be made of the fact that David became my teacher during that time, often adopting your tone of voice to criticize me. He made me practise, he threw up his arms in exasperation when I failed to do the music justice, he tried in vain to curb my irresponsible eating and drinking habits. '*Much* better,' he said, when he was satisfied. It will seem inconceivable to you that David threw away at least two years of his career in order to help me with my own. But do you know what, Geoffrey? David thought he owed me at least that much. Chanat could have used a friend like that.

David will return, rest assured of that. We will pack our bags and re-enter the arena, and David will shine. It will be my turn again to watch from the wings. The Chanat 'Miniatures' will get the public airing they deserve. The deal is done, but still secret; I see no way that you could profit from our imminent coup, so I have no qualms about revealing it to you now. Other than my wife, only one person knows of our project: Igor Malechievich stood in as technical adviser whenever he was in town. Chanat could have used a friend like Igor. He would send you his regards. Last time your name came up, he said, 'I remember. The Englishman who conducts on tippy-toe.'

My visitor has arrived. He has brought supplies for a good meal on the terrace. Tomorrow he will sweep me out of the mountains in his powerful new car. Back to Paris we'll go, rested and alert. My visitor would like to say hello.

Hello, Geoffrey.

David is a man of few words, but I am certain he would want to join me in saying that we are still out here, we are practising hard, and we promise to give a good account of ourselves.

Best wishes,

Pierre Marie La Valoise.